THE EXPERTS HAD WARNED
OF A SUPER QUAKE—
AND NOW IT WAS HAPPENING . . .

First a slight tremor from the treacherous San Andreas Fault—and then in a dirt trench two scientists lay buried beneath the rubble. When the second tremor came, the populace began to panic. And then when the quake hit in all its savage fury, the entire city of Los Angeles faced destruction!

Now, for the first time, the devastation of a great metropolis and its inhabitants is captured on the screen in all its awesome violence. Here, in book form, is a fascinating inside look behind the filming of a super-spectacular: the stars, the stunts, the incredible special effects. And here, brought vividly to life, is the story of the menace which at any moment could destroy the whole State of California!

EARTHQUAKE
The Story of a Movie

SIGNET Movie Editions

☐ **THE THREE MUSKETEERS by Alexandre Dumas.** Exclusive movie edition of the bestselling adventure saga of all time. Includes 8 pages of memorable stills from the 20th Century-Fox film, starring Oliver Reed, Raquel Welch, Richard Chamberlain, Michael York, Frank Finlay, Christopher Lee, Geraldine Chaplin, Simon Ward, Jean-Pierre Cassel, Faye Dunaway and Charlton Heston.
(#Y5935—$1.25)

☐ **THE WHITE DAWN by James Houston.** The nationwide bestseller is now a magnificent Paramount Picture, starring Warren Oates, Timothy Bottoms and Lou Gosset in a story of three white men who are rescued from shipwreck by an isolated Eskimo tribe and are allowed to live with the natives. Here is what happens as two alien cultures move inexorably on a collision course. . . . "A vivid, boiling adventure of savage excitement and sensual delights . . . powerful and beautiful."—**Chicago Sun Times** (#Y5926—$1.25)

☐ **WHERE THE LILIES BLOOM by Vera and Bill Cleaver.** In the tradition of **True Grit,** a poignant, delightful novel of an irrepressible 14-year-old who vows to hold her family together, no matter what. Now a triumphant United Artists movie, introducing Julie Gholson and Harry Dean Stanton. **Where the Lilies Bloom** is the Newberry Award Honor book which the New York Times called "One of the year's most notable books."
(#Y5853—$1.25)

☐ **ZARDOZ, a novel by John Boorman with Bill Stair.** Complete with 8 pages of scenes from the sensational new 20th Century-Fox film starring Sean Connery, the odyssey of Zed the Warrior in the barbarian future—caught between the Brutals and Eternals in a battle for the world! (#Q5830—95¢)

EARTHQUAKE

The Story of a Movie

BY

George Fox

The Film
EARTHQUAKE
was written by
GEORGE FOX
and
MARIO PUZO

SIGNET FILM SERIES

A SIGNET BOOK

NEW AMERICAN LIBRARY

TIMES MIRROR

SIGNET TRADEMARK REG. U.S. PAT. OFF. AND FOREIGN COUNTRIES
REGISTERED TRADEMARK—MARCA REGISTRADA
HECHO EN CHICAGO, U.S.A.

SIGNET, SIGNET CLASSICS, MENTOR, PLUME AND MERIDIAN BOOKS
are published by The New American Library, Inc.,
1301 Avenue of the Americas, New York, New York 10019

FIRST PRINTING, DECEMBER, 1974

1 2 3 4 5 6 7 8 9

PRINTED IN THE UNITED STATES OF AMERICA

For Steve and Karen

EARTHQUAKE

The Story

1

Many experts believe that a cataclysmic earthquake is inevitable in California within the next decade. At two critical points, the sides of the 600-mile-long San Andreas Fault are locked, permitting no slippage. One is north of San Francisco; the other, just a few miles east of Los Angeles. For years, in these areas, the land has been compressed and warped, storing energy like a colossal spring.

2

The city of Los Angeles begins a new day. Among the earliest risers is Stewart Graff. A rugged man in his early forties, Graff lives in a neighborhood of luxurious homes in the hills above the Hollywood Reservoir dam. As he takes his usual morning exercise, jogging along a high trail, the Hollywood area is spread out below: thousands of small homes, towering office buildings, miles of freeways. Because of trees planted at the base of the dam, some of the millions of people in the reservoir's flood path are unaware that it exists.

Remy, Graff's tall, strikingly beautiful wife, watches through a bedroom mirror as he jogs up to the rear of the house. The childless couple have been married since both graduated from the University of Southern California, where he was a football star. Graff then went to work as an engineer for Remy's father, the owner of a major construction company. Although she knows that he has risen by his own efforts to the vice-presidency of the firm, Remy nonetheless goads Graff with having "married the boss's daughter." They are on the verge of separating.

She goes to Graff's dressing room and accuses him of having an affair with Denise Marshall, the young widow of an engineer killed the year before in the collapse of a tunnel project supervised by Graff. Denise has recently returned to Los Angeles after spending seven months with her family back East. Graff has been helping her get resettled. Angered by Remy's baseless charge, Graff deliberately tells her that he is stopping off at Denise's house on the way to work. He has promised her nine-year-old son Corry a football autographed by sports celebrity Frank Gifford. Enraged, Remy leaves the room.

Graff showers and dresses, enters Remy's bedroom. She lies motionless across the bed, breathing harshly. An empty bottle with a barbiturate prescription label is on the night table. He tries to rouse her, fails, runs for the telephone, calls James Vance, their doctor. As he turns back toward the bed, a minor earth tremor shakes the room. Remy sits upright, frightened and totally conscious. Realizing that he has been tricked, Graff stares at her in icy rage . . .

This is only the latest of a series of "suicide attempts" by Remy. Dr. Vance admits that he always suspected the earlier pill overdoses were also faked, and unintentionally reveals that Remy's single pregnancy, years before, had been terminated by an abortion, not an accidental miscarriage as Graff had been told by his wife. Remy bursts in on them, concedes that she had never wanted children. Angrier than ever, Graff takes the autographed football and leaves the house, drives off in the customized four-wheel-drive vehicle he uses to visit construction sites.

Stewart Graff calls his office on his car telephone to say that he will be late. His father-in-law, Sam Royce, is talking to the receptionist when the call comes in. The graying, powerfully built company president takes the phone. He tells Graff to see him as soon as he arrives. The two men have been arguing over the plans for a new office building contracted by Bill Cameron, an important client. Graff feels that the design is too weak for an earthquake zone.

"If Cameron goes ahead, it's with another engineer, not me," Graff declares firmly.

"We'll talk about it again later," Royce replies. "I don't want to blow this contract."

3

Meanwhile, at the reservoir, the caretaker and his young assistant are completing a routine check of the dam, mandatory after a tremor. The caretaker has descended in an elevator to the dam's interior. The assistant, after inspecting the exterior base, goes to the elevator turret, is puzzled to discover that the caretaker is still below. He pushes the "up" button, and the cage rises. The doors open, sending a torrent of water gushing over the turret floor. The caretaker's drowned body spills out with it . . .

4

Graff hears a siren behind him, pulls to the side of the road as a sports car roars past. Pursuing it in a high-speed chase is a Los Angeles squad car. At the wheel is Patrolman Lew Slade, a towering, rawboned man. Beside him is his partner, Emilio Rodriguez. "Watch it, will you, Lew?" Emilio asks nervously as they skid around a corner. "Nearly racked us up that last turn!"

Without replying, Slade steps harder on the gas, narrowing the gap between themselves and the careening sports car. A moment later they cross the city line. "Captain'll bust our rumps if we mess up here in the county again," Emilio groans. "Remember what happened with that guy Merle? I still don't think his gun went off by accident."

"I get along great with nine toes," Slade replies grimly.

A county patrol car joins the chase, racing behind Slade's vehicle. The pursuit ends when the sports car shoots off the road, embeds itself in a luxurious hedge. The driver scrambles over the hedge and flees. Emilio draws his revolver and follows. Before Slade can join his partner, he is overtaken by one of the county cops: Merle, his old nemesis. Merle grabs him by the shoulder, snarls: "You know who owns that hedge you just wrecked? Zsa Zsa Gabor!"

Slade stares at Merle in disbelief, then smashes him in the mouth with a brutal right hook.

5

Miles away, scientists at the California Seismological Institute are checking out data on that morning's small quake. Half the room is taken up by banks of seismographs, recording disturbances all around the globe. Walt Russell—a graduate assistant—hangs up the phone after unsuccessfully trying to reach Dr. Frank Adams upstate. He looks deeply troubled.

Russell nervously approaches Dr. Harvey Johnson, a deputy director of the institute. He tells Johnson that he sent some figures and a memo into the director's office the previous day. "I wish Dr. Adams was here to back up my computations," he says.

"Computations on what?"

Knowing he won't be believed, Russell replies: "I think we're going to have a really big quake. Probably today. Tomorrow at the latest . . ."

At that very moment, geologist Adams prepares the final steps of a research project in an isolated rural section of Central California. He and a graduate assistant are sinking instruments in the bottom of a ditch dug across the San Andreas Fault. While they are planting the last of their seismic measuring devices, the walls of the ditch collapse, burying them beneath tons of earth. No one has witnessed their deaths. . . .

6

In the kitchen of her small rented house below the dam, Denise Marshall cleans up crockery broken by the tremor. She is a slim, delicately lovely girl in her late twenties. "Remember to go to Mrs. Clark's next door when you get out of school," she tells her son Corry, who is cramming papers into his book bag. "She'll look after you until I'm home from the studio."

The doorbell rings. Denise admits Stewart Graff, who tosses the football to the eager Corry. "Sorry I forgot last week," Graff says.

"You really shouldn't have, Stewart," Denise says when Corry leaves for school.

"Couldn't let down my last fan," Graff replies.

Denise, an actress before her marriage, tells Graff that she has found her first job since returning to Los Angeles, a small part in a movie. "When you've been out of the business so long, it's hard getting reestablished," she says. "But at least I feel alive again. I didn't for a long time after Brian died."

Graff remains for coffee. While the water is boiling, he feeds Denise rehearsal lines from her film scene. In the movie story, Graff's character is attempting to seduce her. Denise's manner of reading hints that she wishes he were trying it in real life. "Only one thing bothers me," Denise says with a laugh. "The character I play is supposed to be a nymphomaniac, and the director of the picture is a strong believer in typecasting. Anyway, it's a living, and I think it's time I took off my widow's weeds, don't you?"

He is obviously jarred by the implication that Denise is considering an affair. She catches his look, smiles wryly. "Don't worry," she murmurs, "I'm not a nympho. I'm not Mary Poppins, but I'm far from a nympho."

Denise is late for her movie call. She kisses Graff quickly on the cheek, rushes out, leaves him to finish his coffee. He glances after her, a sense of sudden, disturbed understanding in his eyes.

Corry, riding his bicycle to school, takes a short cut through a wooded section, comes upon an open field. Scattered about are the unassembled fragments of an intricate motorcycle daredevil act: giant loop-the-loops, steep wooden ramps, other gear. Two men are putting the rig together. The trick cyclist, Miles Quade, is an athletic-looking black, dressed in a vinyl costume decorated with golden lightning bolts. His mechanic, Sal Amici, wears greasy coveralls.

"You sure we can set everything up by four thirty, Sal?" Miles asks his friend. At that hour a promoter from a Las Vegas hotel is auditioning their new act.

"Yeah. But I'm still not sure Rosa will help us out. Ain't exactly crazy about our line of work."

"She better," Miles replies. "This Vegas job is the biggest break we ever had."

7

At the Hollywood reservoir, an inspection team is trying to determine how the caretaker died in the dam's elevator. A scuba diver breaks the surface after checking the inner concrete wall. "All okay as far as I can tell," he cries up to the chief inspector, standing with the assistant caretaker atop the dam.

The chief inspector nods toward a pump truck parked outside the elevator turret. "Guess we won't know what happened until the shaft is drained," he remarks. "But everything looks fine."

"Sure, buddy," snaps the still-shaken assistant. "People drown in elevators every damned day of the week."

8

In a nearby police station, Lew Slade is being chewed out by his precinct captain for slugging Merle, the county cop. "Eight stitches to close his lower lip!" the captain rages. "Six loosened teeth!"

Defiant, Slade reminds the captain that he and Emilio had been pursuing a hit-and-run driver when the incident occurred. "That guy stole a car," he growls. "Then he slammed into a little girl—Mexican girl about six years old. The little girl was thrown maybe fifteen feet in the air. Probably dead before she hit the sidewalk. And the driver damned near got away because a peckerwood rich man's whore in a cop's uniform was worried about a hedge!"

The captain shakes his head. "You'll receive a formal notice of suspension, a date for departmental trial. Now get on home."

In the hall outside, Emilio is waiting to book the hit-and-run driver. "Lew, how'd it go?" he asks as Slade strides past. Slade makes a thumbs-down gesture. He stops by the entrance to the department property office, starts to unbuckle his gun belt, then changes his mind and leaves the station.

At a small supermarket two doors down the street, Jody, the store's manager, is arguing with a group of Hare Krishna disciples who are chanting and ringing their prayer bells on the sidewalk. He is a lean, intense-looking young man with long, bushy brown hair. "All right, you freeloading creeps, clear out!" he bellows, gets no response from the beatifically smiling disciples.

Jody spots Slade approaching, grabs his arm. "Officer, could you order these kids to move on?" he asks. "They're scaring people away from the store."

"You got something against religion?" Slade says, glaring.

Inside the market, Sal Amici's nineteen-year-old sister Rosa discovers at the checkout counter that she has forgotten her wallet. Dark and voluptuous, she radiates an almost childlike pride in her own beauty. All around the store signs further-proclaim: CREDIT IS DEAD—DON'T ASK FOR IT. Nevertheless, Jody tells Rosa that she can drop off the money the next time she comes in. The checkout girl glances at him in astonishment. Jody's gaze, full of suppressed desire, trails Rosa as she carries her groceries from the store.

9

Dr. Willis Stockle, director of the Seismology Institute, sits at his desk, going over Walt Russell's notes. Stockle is a sixtyish, reserved man with weathered features. He doesn't look up when the hesitant Russell enters the office and says: "You sent for me, Dr. Stockle?"

"This is all very interesting," Stockle says drily. "You forecast an earthquake in the three-to-four-point range this morning, and we had an earthquake in the three-to-four-point range. I'm impressed. However, isn't it rather slim evidence for predicting catastrophe?"

Russell tells Stockle that his data were based on signals from stress-measurement devices planted under Dr. Adams's guidance. The latest figures, taken that morning, indicate a second preshock before noon.

"And if it happens?" Stockle asks.

"The big one follows within forty-eight hours," Russell says. "At least seven points on the Richter scale."

"Are you seriously contending that a graduate student has become the first scientist in history to pinpoint a major earthquake within forty-eight hours?" Stockle barks.

Russell nervously replies that he is only following Dr. Adams's theories. He has still been unable to reach Adams. After dismissing Russell, Stockle studies the data with a skeptical but slightly troubled frown. Then he lifts the phone and says to his secretary: "I want some figures run through the computer. And try to get me Frank Adams in Fresno."

10

Sam Royce visits his son-in-law's office a few minutes after he finally arrives at his office. Graff is staring broodingly out of the window, studying the hills above the reservoir dam. "You still refuse to handle the Cameron job unless he upgrades the specifications?" Royce asks.

"Absolutely."

"Okay," Royce says reluctantly. "But it's up to you to convince Cameron the changes are necessary."

The company has contracted for a hydroelectric project in Oregon. As he has often before, Graff tells Royce that he wants to head up the job. "I was never cut out to be a desk man," he says. "Not for this long a stretch."

Royce finally agrees to give Graff the assignment. He goes to his office, where his attractive blonde secretary Barbara informs him that Remy is on the phone. "Please, Dad, I have to see you," Remy pleads. "It's terribly important," They agree to meet for lunch at one fifteen. Royce looks troubled as he hangs up the phone.

Slade enters a neighborhood bar. In the back of the room, four men are shooting pool for high stakes. One has a sheaf of bills in his hand, paying off on a game. He tries to hide the money when he sees the policeman. Slade waves at them to continue, sits at the bar.

"Double bourbon, Jay," he tells the bartender.

The bartender hesitates. "In uniform, Lew?"

"Naked in a glass will do fine."

Slade, his face angry and resentful, downs his drink.

Just then, the second small tremor predicted by Walt Russell hits. One of the pool players in the saloon, a muscular giant of a man, is making a shot. His cue misses by inches. When the tremor subsides, he argues that the shot didn't count. Another player insists that it does. The two grapple, fall to the floor.

Emilio enters, sits beside Slade at the bar. "Captain's cooled off," he tells Slade, who has now had several drinks. "He's gonna do his damnedest to straighten things out."

Slade shakes his head. "I don't want to be a cop anymore, Emilio. Right from the time I was a kid, I thought about cops as helping people. But people don't count anymore, do they? Hedges count!"

As the two policemen talk, the battle between the pool players grows more violent. Emilio leaves, unable to reason with his friend. Slade goes over to the fighting men. He grabs the giant by the collar, throws him across the room. "The shot counted," Slade announces.

11

Dr. Stockle, Johnson, and Walt Russell confer in the doctor's office over the significance of the second shock. Johnson believes it was coincidental. Stockle, who has personally checked Russell's figures, feels that the danger of a major quake exists. "Which brings us to the present problem," he says. "What in the name of God do we do now?"

"Warn people," says the puzzled Russell.

Stockle reminds him that public announcement of a big tremor would trigger panic. More people might die in the crush to flee the city than would be killed in an earthquake. And if they issue a warning and a shock doesn't occur, the institute's credibility would be damaged. "Suppose we come up with a foolproof detection system five years from now?" Stockle asks. "Who would believe us?"

They are still arguing when Stockle gets word that Dr. Frank Adams has been killed in a cave-in at the fault. The seismologist's sacrifice of his life to his work tips the balance. Stockle has his secretary put a phone call through to the mayor.

12

Remy and her father meet for lunch at a restaurant. She tells Royce that she is certain Graff and Denise Marshall, whom she has never met, are lovers. "But he can't walk out on me if you make him company president," she says. "He'd be walking out on his career, too."

"Won't work, Remy," Royce says. "When you met Stewart, he was a dirt-poor kid on an athletic scholarship. You *still* half see him that way. But now he doesn't need you, and he doesn't need me. Not a firm in town won't take him on his own terms."

"I'll never ask anything of you again," Remy begs. "Please, Dad, please!"

Shaken by Remy's desperation, Royce is unable to reply.

Restless, Stewart Graff leaves his office, encounters Denise in the building's lobby. She tells him that the second tremor damaged the set of her movie, that the scenes have been rescheduled for the next day. With time on her hands, she decided to drop in on Barbara, a friend from the days when Denise's husband worked for the company.

"I need a drink," Graff says. "Will you join me?"

They leave the building together.

13

At Los Angeles City Hall, Dr. Stockle has told the mayor about Walt Russell's prediction. "How big a quake?" the mayor asks incredulously.

"At least seven on the Richter scale," Stockle replies somberly. "Releasing more than the total energy generated by the Hiroshima and Nagasaki nuclear bombs combined."

"If I issue a public warning, do you know what will happen to this city?" says the stunned official.

Stockle agrees that this course is impossible. However, he advises the mayor to put the police and fire departments on alert, ask the governor to mobilize the National Guard. Since the second tremor caused extensive property damage in the San Fernando Valley, it would serve as an excuse for a guard call-up.

Although doubtful of the need, the mayor agrees to these precautions.

14

Miles, Sal, and Rosa enter the neighborhood saloon. Rosa is now dressed in a vinyl costume—tight black pants and boots, zippered jacket—similar to Miles's gaudy clothing. Reluctantly, she has agreed to take part in the stunt demonstration for the Las Vegas promoter.

While Rosa visits the ladies room, Miles and Sal amble up to the bar, order three hamburgers to go. Miles recognizes Slade, claps him on the shoulder. "Hey, Lew!" he shouts cheerfully. "Still pursuing evildoers?"

The giant pool player turns at the sound of Miles's voice, scowls. Holding his reversed cue like a club, he comes over, stares threateningly at the cyclist. "The fifty," he growls. "You've owed me three weeks. You are a great bike rider but a lousy pool shooter."

"You going to let him get away with this?" Miles asks Slade.

"Yes."

Miles pays up, discovers that he lacks enough money to buy a tank of propane needed for the act. He asks Slade to loan him ten dollars, is turned down. Rosa returns to the bar, and Sal introduces her to Slade, adding: "He's the cop who laid out me and Miles with a blackjack at the North Hollywood rally last year. Some ruckus."

"You should have knocked their brains into place," Rosa snaps.

Rosa and Sal quarrel over her remark. He is barely able to keep her from leaving. "Daredevil motorcyclists always have beautiful, sexy broads hanging around,"

Miles cuts in. "You want this Las Vegas guy to think I'm a phony?"

Miles urges her to show Slade the special T-shirt he has designed for the act. "We're gonna have thirty, forty thousand made up after the Vegas show," he says.

Rosa throws open her jacket. Beneath it she wears a tight T-shirt decorated with lightning bolts and the name MILES. Her huge, shapely, braless breasts seem to leap at Slade through the flimsy material. He is transfixed.

"What do you think?" Miles asks.

"I think it's beautiful," Slade says. He takes out his wallet, hands bills to Miles, still staring raptly at Rosa.

After leaving the office building, Stewart Graff and Denise went to her home. They have made love with desperate urgency, giving way to a need neither had acknowledged until today. Now Denise sits on a vanity chair in her bedroom, brushing her hair. She glances over her shoulder at Graff, sprawled on the bed. "When you said 'I need a drink,' I had a hunch that wasn't all you needed," she says. "May I ask you something?"

"Anything."

"You made love with such . . . anger. Why?"

"Don't be hurt," Graff says. "I learned something today. It made me furious—at my wife. Not at you."

Denise smiles. "The effect was fine. In fact, I'm awarding you the game ball. Anyway, you didn't seduce me. I seduced you. Ever know me to 'drop in' on Barbara before? I wanted to see *you.*"

"Come here," he orders gently. Denise lies beside him on the bed, and they kiss, long and hard. "I'll be in Oregon most of the summer," he says. "Hydroelectric project. Why don't you and Corry come up? I'll rent a house for the two of you."

"I'll think about it," she murmurs.

"And I'll be back tonight."

She strokes his hair. "I'll think about that, too."

The mayor's secret disaster plan has gone into operation. Off-duty policemen have been called back. Puzzled and bored, officers sit around the emergency control center at Los Angeles headquarters, doing nothing. Among those affected by the plan is Jody, the supermarket manager. He is manning the register at a checkout counter when word comes over the radio that several guard units are being called up. Without a word he removes his white apron and leaves the store, while surprised customers peer after him.

Jody drives to the seedy rooming house where he lives. Loafing on the front steps are three insolent-looking youths: Buck, Sandy, and Ralph. Jody tenses when he sees them, his expression growing stony. "Where're them cantaloupes?" Buck taunts him.

"What's the good of having a buddy in a supermarket if he don't bring you free cantaloupes?" Ralph adds.

Jody, without speaking, walks past the hecklers, climbs the stairs to his top floor room. Scotch-taped to the walls are photographs of weight lifters. Light barbells and other body-building equipment lie on the floor. He goes into the closet, puts on sharply pressed GI fatigues with sergeant first-class stripes on the sleeves. As he dresses, he stares at a magazine centerfold of a nude brunette, tacked to the inside closet door. She resembles Rosa Amici.

He slips a close-cropped blond wig over his scraggly brown hair, leaves the closet, just as Buck, Sandy, and Ralph swagger into the room. "Is it true blonds have more fun?" Bucks says with a sneer when he notices the wig.

"Always told you he was a fag," Ralph says, glancing at the weight-lifter photos.

Trembling with anger, Jody strides into the hall, starts down the stairs. The trio follows him in mock military formation. They reach a filled garbage can outside an apartment door. Buck picks it up, throws the contents at Jody, on the landing below. Although garbage splatters over his uniform, he continues on.

"Maybe we better let up on Jody," Ralph says as they watch their victim drive off. "He don't talk back. I'm kind of nervous about guys who don't talk back."

Buck scoffs at him, then adds thoughtfully: "If things got so screwed up in the valley quake, let's head over and take a look. Might be good stuff lying around . . ."

15

The water level has risen two more inches at the Hollywood dam. The assistant caretaker is staring apprehensively at the indicator when the chief inspector joins him. "Department just called me back," the inspector says with relief. "They found the trouble. A lock on one of the reservoir feeder canals jammed open during the tremor. No way to regulate the flow until they fix it."

"Gonna be an awful lot of pressure on this old hunk of concrete in a few hours," the assistant comments glumly.

16

Miles, Sal, and Rosa have gone to the field, where Sal completes setting up the equipment for the stunt. Proudly, Miles explains the run to Rosa. "I start up on that high platform over there," he says. "Hit the forty-foot vertical loop at eighty miles an hour ... Run into the figure-eight horizontal loops ... Zoom up the first ramp, sail clear over the truck, shoot through the fiery ring! Not just fire on the outside, like in dog acts! The gas jets fill the whole middle with flames! Up another ramp and over that pit filled with sharpened stakes! Home free! Evel Knievel flies over twenty, thirty cars and makes a big thing of it! Compared to those stakes, landing on a car roof at one hundred miles per is like diving on a waterbed!"

Rosa is appalled. "Miles, you are out ... of ... your ... mind!" she gasps.

She refuses to take any part in the stunt. "No way," she tells her brother. "If you want to help your best friend kill himself, fine! But I don't have to be here to see it! I'm going to a movie. The Clint Eastwood at the Royale."

Despite Miles's protests that the stunt is easy, Rosa hurries away from the field.

Stewart Graff has returned to his office, where he meets with Bill Cameron, the businessman who has contracted for a high-rise office building. Using a model and a vibrating platform, he shows Cameron that the proposed design would be under dangerous stress in an earthquake, even though it meets existing building codes. "You'd risk losing my business over something like this?" Cameron asks.

"Yes," Graff replies.

Before the discussion goes further, a young engineer named Carl Leeds enters the office, tells Cameron that the blueprints of the building's interior have just arrived. Cameron goes off with Carl to inspect them.

Sam Royce comes in, offers Graff the presidency of the company. "That title 'chairman of the board' always appealed to me," Royce says. "You'll have to give up the Oregon project, naturally."

Graff hesitates. "You'll figure I'm crazy, Sam," he says slowly, "but I'd like a little time to think over the offer."

"Some problem I ought to be told about?"

"Just a few priorities to get straight in my head ... Did Remy have anything to do with this?"

"Don't worry," Royce replies. "You'd have the job even if you weren't my son-in-law."

Graff calls Denise when Royce leaves the office. He tells her that they won't be able to meet that night. "It doesn't matter, darling," she says. "We'll have lots of time together—up in Oregon. Good-bye."

Corry, home from school, asks permission to ride his bike to the local playground. "All right," Denise says. "But be careful crossing that bridge," Restless, troubled by something in Graff's tone, she decides to take a walk ...

As a pair of window washers work outside his twentieth-floor office, Sam Royce dictates a letter to Barbara. He breaks off, says to his secretary: "You were friendly with Brian Marshall. Ever meet his wife?"

Barbara nods. "A nice girl."

"I was afraid of that," Royce sighs.

The receptionist buzzes, announces that Remy is

outside. "Did you talk to Stewart?" Remy asks anxiously as she hurries into the office. Barbara leaves.

"He'll take the job," Royce assures his daughter.

Graff bursts into Sam Royce's office. "You've got yourself a new president," he tells Royce before he notices Remy standing by the window. Her shoulders slump with relief as she turns toward him.

"And you'll stay away from Denise Marshall?" she cries.

Graff's features tighten angrily. "Sam didn't tell me that was a condition."

He leaves Royce's office. Remy impulsively follows him into the hall, on to an unoccupied elevator. "Why are you so furious?" she asks.

"Remy, can't you understand? It was another bribe! Our whole marriage has been a series of bribes!"

"You took them," she says. "You're going to that Marshall bitch, aren't you?"

"Not until tonight."

"You finally admit the truth, then?"

"This morning it wasn't the truth," Graff says. "This afternoon, it is. It's going to continue to be."

The argument temporarily ceases when the elevator halts at a lower floor and several people come aboard . . .

A sedan pulls into the field where Sal and Miles have set up their rig. "Here he is," Sal says. "The guy from Vegas."

Miles has already tested the course, is supremely sure of himself. "This is going to be the greatest run of my life," he declares. "I'm tuned to exactly the right pitch!"

He and Sal hasten over to greet the promoter . . .

Denise has left the house, is walking along a dirt trail. Atop a steep ridge above her sits a row of typical Los Angeles stilt homes, their girder-supported rear decks projecting into space. A man on one of the decks is eating a chicken leg. He sees Denise hundreds of feet below, waves cheerfully. Suddenly dogs begin howling. Hundreds of unaccountably frightened birds fly out of the trees. Denise halts, looks around in puzzlement.

17

At the dam, the chief inspector and the assistant care-taker are listening to a diver who has just examined the elevator shaft where the caretaker drowned hours ear-lier. "Finally found the trouble," the diver says. "Old conduit busted, flooded the bottom of the shaft."

"Nothing worse?" asks the inspector.

The words are barely out of his mouth when a new tremor hits, builds in intensity. The most terrible earth-quake in history has begun. The dam workers are knocked off their feet. An eerie rumbling fills the air, as if a fearsome, invisible avalanche is falling from the cloudless California sky.

18

Miles Quade is atop the platform, racing his motorcycle, just about to start his run. He watches in astonishment as the loop-the-loops topple, the fiery ring falls and sputters out like a match, the ramps disintegrate into piles of loose boards. Sal and the promoter are thrown to the ground. Then the platform collapses. Miles and his machine spiral to earth. . . .

Graff and Remy have reached the parking lot next to the office building. Huge chunks of debris rain from the skies, smashing in car roofs, killing and injuring dozens of people. Graff grabs Remy, who is paralyzed with fear, rolls both of them under his four-wheel-drive vehicle . . .

19

With incredible speed, the city of Los Angeles virtually disintegrates. The earth tilts and is torn apart, creating crevasses that swallow hundreds of screaming men and women. High buildings crumble into rubble and dust. Elevated freeways collapse, dropping cars and trucks to destruction below ...

...

20

Corry is pedaling his bike on a narrow wooden bridge
across the dry bed of the Los Angeles river. The bridge
shakes, buckles in the middle. The child is flung from
his bike. He rolls down a tilted section of bridge,
crashes to the paved riverbed, lies unconscious, his
forehead bloody. High-voltage electric towers on both
sides of the river turn into twisted masses of steel. One
topples on a smaller utility pole, which in turn falls on
the bridge wreckage. Its wires are stretched taut but
don't break ...

Denise holds on to a tree trunk with both arms as
the ground rocks beneath her. The stilt-supported
houses on the hill break up as their underbeams collapse. Denise releases her grip on the tree, runs frantically as wreckage falls all about her. She is almost hit
by a refrigerator, zooming down the slope like a tobog-
gan. The body of the man with the chicken leg follows
seconds later ...

Sam Royce is thrown against the wall of his office. He
sees the window washers scream in terror as their scaffold swings back and forth, crashing through the glass.
Royce staggers over, tries to help the men get inside. He
is too late. The scaffold ropes snap and they are pitched
into space ...

Bill Cameron flees Carl Leeds's office, runs for the elevators. He brutally shoves Barbara out of the way, pushes himself into an overloaded car. The elevator starts down, shuddering and scraping with every convulsion. It comes to a halt, shakes violently. The cables break, and the car plunges twenty floors, its occupants literally plastered to the ceiling . . .

At the top of the elevator shaft, the strained mechanism runs wild. A gear wheel flies free at terrific speed, crashes through a partition into the room where the air-conditioning system is housed. The red-hot wheel starts a fire in the system, igniting liquid freon. A pale vapor—deadly phosgene gas—is released . . .

The seismological institute is devastated by the quake. Russell, Stockle, and the other scientists are crushed by debris. Every seismic chart has gone crazy, producing wild patterns of black lines . . .

Almost as hard hit is the neighborhood saloon. The pool table shoots across the room, squashes half a dozen patrons against the bar. Slade and the other drinkers have fallen off their stools. Beer and club soda faucets shoot their liquids in high arcs . . .

The police station down the street crumbles, killing everyone inside, including Emilio . . .

On a Hollywood business street, frightened customers dash out of a movie house. Rosa is one of them. The theater marquee breaks loose from the building, crashes down on many of the patrons. Rose narrowly escapes being crushed . . .

Blocks away, a man rushes to the front door of his small frame home, hoping to save some of his belongings. He carries a cigarette. "Turn off your gas!" a stranger calls to him. The man continues into the house. An instant later it explodes with a fiery roar . . .

21

*The bells in a church tower carillon clang chaotically.
Then, as the great earthquake subsides, the sounds
change to a low tolling. Finally silence falls—total and
eerie. The city is devastated, the entire Los Angeles ba-
sin covered with swirling dust clouds, dotted by the
glow of scattered fires ...*

22

Stewart Graff helps Remy crawl out from beneath the vehicle. The ground is covered with rubble. He stares up at his office building. "My God!" he cries. "Stay here!" He runs toward the building. Remy has followed his gaze. She winces in horror.

Above, in the construction company offices, Sam Royce holds Barbara in his arms, patting her back. "Mr. Cameron just shoved me out of the way," Barbara says in a dazed voice. "Before I could get on the elevator—"

"Settle down now. It's all over."

Royce and Barbara go into the large central office, where he attempts to calm the employees. They resemble shock victims. Royce has restored order when a young secretary, sitting below an air-conditioning outlet, slips to the floor unconscious. A male executive standing nearby collapses on his knees, coughing uncontrollably.

"It's phosgene!" Royce exclaims, seeing the fumes pouring from the outlet.

Most of the workers panic, run for the door. Royce picks up the overcome secretary. Barbara helps the fallen executive. By the time they reach the fire stairs, dozens of employees are fleeing ahead of them. The men and women in the lead round a corner—and discover too late that a huge chunk of the building has fractured. The broken stairway falls off into empty space! Shrieking in fear, they try to halt. But the pressure of the people behind pushes half a dozen over the edge. They drop to their deaths.

Graff has run up the fire stairs. He reaches the lower section of the break just as the doomed office workers hurtle past. Fifty feet above, others brace themselves against walls, frantically trying to keep from being shoved into the fracture . . .

Meanwhile, Denise has reached her house. The garage has collapsed, burying her car beneath debris. She throws open the front door, rushes inside, calling for Corry. There is no sign of the child. She decides to go to the playground, the last place she knew Corry had been . . .

The police emergency-control center has been crippled by the quake; most of the officers on duty, killed or injured. However, by the time the mayor arrives at the center, technicians are setting up mobile field radios. "Is there any way I can broadcast to the whole city, get picked up on transistor sets?" he asks a technician.

"A few commercial stations on the quake fringe area are still operating. Might be able to rig a microwave relay to one of them."

"Get on it, then!" the mayor orders . . .

Lew Slade, though half drunk himself, tries to restore order in the saloon. He lifts the pool table off the injured patrons, shouts for help from the stunned players. They shakily come to his aid. Realizing his condition, Slade staggers into the men's room, shoves his head under a broken pipe spouting water . . .

23

On top of Hollywood dam, the inspection crew members pick themselves up. "It held!" the chief inspector shouts in relief.

"How much longer?" the assistant caretaker asks. "I'm going to divert water into the spillways! We have to get the pressure down!"

"Not without official permission," the inspector replies. "The city will need every drop we can give it. Dozens of fires already."

Ignoring the inspector, the assistant goes into the turret, starts trying to turn the manual valve diverting water from the reservoir into the Los Angeles river. The valve is frozen. When the inspector tries to stop him, he barks: "If this dam busts, won't be nothing between here and Wilshire Boulevard left to burn!"

The inspector helps the assistant with the valve. It still won't budge.

24

At the shattered office building, Graff and Sam Royce have formed a plan to get the upper-floor survivors to the lower stairs before they are overcome by gas. Royce and Carl Leeds bring a swivel chair from an inner office. Running a fire hose from the hallway, they attach it to the chair, creating a crude lifting device. The semiconscious secretary, secured to the chair with pantyhose, is the first to make the descent, dropped to Graff by Royce and the other men, muscles straining as they slowly play out the hose. When the chair is at Graff's level, he pulls it onto the stairway. He unties the secretary, eases her onto the steps, sends the chair up again ...

On her way to the playground, Denise reaches the bridge across the dry riverbed. She sees Corry lying unconscious on the cement, six feet below the splintered end of the collapsed bridge section. Carefully, she crawls down the slanted boards. She accidentally dislodges a chunk of wreckage supporting the toppled utility pole. The pole slips a few feet more, and the taut wires snap. The writhing, sputtering ends fall all around Corry, missing him by inches.

Denise drops to the riverbed, threads her way through the wires, lifts Corry in her arms, carries him back to the bridge. However, she has no way of raising his limp form up to the broken section. She cries out for help. Unknown to her, the dam workers have freed the sluice valve, releasing thousands of gallons of water into the river.

Miles and Sal, driving past the river in their truck, hear Denise's shouts. They descend the bridge section, take Corry from her upraised arms, carry him to the truck. Denise, still in the riverbed, sees a sheet of water—four or five inches deep—creeping down the dry channel. Realizing what will happen when it reaches the wires, she makes a desperate leap for the section, gets a risky handhold an instant before the water contacts the sputtering cables, creating a bubbling inferno. She is about to lose her grip when Miles returns and lifts her to safety . . .

Lew Slade—the only cop left alive in the neighborhood—is desperately attempting to maintain order. He has rounded up volunteers to give first aid to the injured. The frightened people are partially calmed when the mayor is faintly heard on transistor radios. He announces that emergency clinics are being set up all over the city. The closest to the neighborhood is a modern skyscraper called Wilson Plaza . . .

At the fractured office building, everyone except Sam Royce has reached the other stairway. Graff, Barbara, and Carl Leeds wait for Royce to shinny down the hose. Graff calls up to him, gets no answer. He leaps onto the dangling hose, climbs it hand by hand to the upper level. He finds Royce lying semiconscious. The air is still thick with gas fumes.

Graff raises the chair, straps Royce into it. "I don't think I'm strong enough to lower you by myself," he says. "So get ready for a jolt."

When the chair is halfway down, Graff loses his grip. Royce plunges more than twenty feet, and the strain pulls the anchored end of the hose halfway from its wall socket. After Carl and Barbara free Royce from the chair, Graff descends. An instant after he reaches the landing, the hose tears loose.

Graff slings Royce over his shoulders, and they start down to the street.

Miles and Sal drive Denise and her injured child toward the police station, not realizing it has been destroyed. They encounter Slade and his volunteers. Slade examines Corry, is unable to bring him around. He commandeers the truck, orders Sal to take Corry and other injured people to Wilson Plaza.

"I got to find my sister," Sal protests. "She went to the movies."

"I'll look for Rosa," Miles says. He mounts his motorcycle, roars off.

As dusk falls over the city, Rosa Amici walks through deserted streets, trying to get back home. She notices the smashed-in front of a small café, sees a stack of rolls on the counter. Hungry, she goes inside, crams rolls into her jacket pockets. Behind the counter, a cash register drawer gapes open, its trays full of money. Rosa turns back toward the door, halts in consternation. Standing there is a young, steel-helmeted man in National Guard fatigues. He carries a rifle.

25

An army helicopter has landed on the dam, where a Corps of Engineers colonel hears reports from the inspection team. He radios to the mayor that the structure is intact. "I'm not taking any chances," the mayor replies. "Dr. Stockle said we could expect aftershocks. Some structures look sound but are so weakened even a minor quake can bring them down. Evacuate the area below the dam . . ."

26

Graff has driven his vehicle to Wilson Plaza. An emergency hospital has been set up in the first of three basement garage levels. He halts on the entrance ramp, where National Guardsmen, nurses, and volunteer doctors are helping the injured. James Vance is among then. He hurries over, examines Royce, lying unconscious in the rear of the vehicle.

"He's had a heart attack," Vance tells Remy and Barbara, who have accompanied Graff.

The women start to follow stretcher bearers carrying Royce off. Then Remy realizes that Graff is still at the wheel. She returns to the vehicle. "Denise and her son will need looking after," Graff says. "If I can find them. Good-bye, Remy. I'm sorry."

"Don't you ever try to come back to me!" Remy shouts as he drives away . . .

In Hollywood, Jody leads his National Guard squad down a business street, lit by flames from dozens of distant fires. They pass a group of civilians—including Rosa—who have been arrested for looting. Jody persuades a corporal guarding the prisoners to turn the girl over to him.

The squad takes up position outside a wrecked appliance store. "Is it all right if I go home?" Rosa asks.

Jody shakes his head. "Can't allow that. Now that it's dark the animals are loose. You just make yourself comfortable inside the store."

49

Nearby, Graff's vehicle and Sal's truck pass each other, going in opposite directions. Denise, caring for Corry in the rear of the truck, fails to notice her lover's car.

A patrol sent out by Jody returns to the appliance store. With them—held at gunpoint—are Buck, Sandy, and Ralph. They have been found with a suitcase full of looted jewelry. Jody cuts down his three former tormentors with a burst of fire from his M-16. "Not like back in the supermarket, is it, Miss Amici?" he shouts to the horrified Rosa. "No scrawny bitches complaining because you won't give them double Green Stamps! Not today!"

Rosa fearfully backs into the store, realizing that Jody is nearly insane. He turns to his shocked men, tells them that no civilians are to be allowed through without being questioned.

Graff has reached Denise's house, found it deserted. He doesn't know that helicopters equipped with loudspeakers have warned everyone to leave the area, directly in the dam's floodpath. All have fled except Slade and a dozen people too seriously hurt to evacuate on foot.

Slade stops Graff's vehicle. "This thing looks like it'll go anywhere, and that's what I need," he says. "Out."

"What are you talking about?" Graff gasps. "I have to find some people."

"You're healthy enough to walk, and I got a lot of injured to move," Slade barks, drawing his revolver. "Out!"

The policeman's plan collapses when he is unable to operate the vehicle, equipped with an intricate, customized transmission system. "Okay, you're an ambulance driver," he declares. "We're going to Wilson Plaza."

Sal has already reached the Plaza and unloaded the injured from his truck. Vance examines Corry, who is still unconscious. "You look done in," he tells Denise. "We've set up a canteen in the third basement shopping arcade. Have a cup of coffee. I'll get word to you, don't worry."

27

Wilson Plaza—operating on its own generators—is one of the few surviving buildings with power.

28

At the bottom of the third-level escalator, Denise encounters Barbara, asks about Graff. "He's fine," Barbara tells the relieved girl. "I'm going up for some air."

Volunteers are handing out coffee, donuts, and other simple foods to hundreds of people in the arcade. The weary Denise joins the line. Remy is only a few places ahead of her.

Up in the first-level garage, Dr. Vance raises his stethoscope from Sam Royce's chest. "He's gone," Vance tells a nurse. "Never had a chance."

"Should I inform his daughter?" the nurse asks.

"Not enough doctors to treat the injured, much less hysteria cases."

Attendants lift Royce's body from the cot. He is instantly replaced by an old woman swathed in bandages . . .

Inside the appliance store, Jody brings Rosa a mess kit filled with food. "It's a hot night," he says, staring at her with disturbing intensity. "Why don't you take off that jacket?" He partially pulls down the zipper, showing part of her revealing MILES T-shirt.

Excited, he removes his steel helmet. She glances at his blond wig. "A lot of guys with hair over regulation length wear them," he says, opening the jacket all the way. "You like me, too, don't you? You never said anything back at the store, but I could tell."

Rosa pushes his hand away. "Don't hurry me," she murmurs warily, her manner softening. "It's no real fun that way . . ."

Two GI stretcher-bearers carry Denise's son through the Wilson Plaza arcade. Vance is with them. Denise rushes up to him. "How is he?" she asks anxiously.

"Just mild shock and a concussion, I think. I'm taking him for X-rays. The Army medics set up a field unit in the third-level garage."

Remy sees Vance, pushes her way through the crowd to confront him. "Why aren't you with my father?" she asks angrily, following them through a door into the garage.

"Don't bother me now!" Vance snaps.

29

Suddenly a seismic aftershock shakes the earth, subsides in seconds. Like a wine glass shattered by sound
waves, Wilson Plaza collapses with a mighty roar, leaving only a steel skeleton. Rivers of debris pour into the
first-basement level—killing everyone—crash down the
escalators into the second and third levels, burying
hundreds. Denise throws herself over Corry as rubble cascades through the garage ramp. The lights go
out . . .

30

Graff and Slade, heading toward Wilson Plaza, halt until the aftershock passes. "More buildings are bound to have come down," Graff says as he drives on. "For the first time in my life I'm ashamed of my profession. We had no right to put up those forty-floor monstrosities. Not here."

They are nearing the patrol area of Jody's squad. Alone with Rosa in the gutted appliance store, he takes a diamond necklace from the looters' suitcase, fastens it around her throat. "That looks great," he says. "A beautiful girl ought to have nice things."

One of Jody's troops enters the store. "Another car coming," he announces.

The guardsmen have halted Graff's vehicle. "This area is quarantined," Jody tells Slade. "You'll have to detour."

"I'm transporting injured people!" Slade bellows.

Rose comes to the store doorway, recognizes Slade. "Lew, help me!" she screams. "He's crazy! Don't leave me with him!"

Opposed by more than a dozen armed men, Graff and Slade turn back. As they drive away, Slade peers up at the rearview mirror, sees Jody shove Rosa into the store.

The uncertain guardsmen glance nervously at each other. "I'm getting an officer," a private says at last.

"That guy in there *has* cracked!" He runs off. The other troops hesitate briefly, flee after him.

"Another hundred feet," Slade tells Graff. "Then stop."

Inside the store, the enraged Jody props his M-16 against the wall. "Crazy, am I?" he yells, slapping Rosa. He rips off her jacket, stares at her T-shirt, the full breasts straining at the cloth. "Only a whore would wear a thing like that!"

Holding his revolver straight down against his leg, Slade enters the store. "Let's go, Rosa" he says. Jody shoves the girl away, grabs his rifle, swings it toward Slade. The policeman fires a single shot. Hit in the chest, the dying Jody crashes to the floor, the blond wig flying from his head.

Slade leads the sobbing Rosa back to the vehicle, cradles her on his lap as they continue toward Wilson Plaza. "Settle down, huh?" he says, patting her shoulder. "Earthquakes bring out the worst in some guys, that's all."

The clumsy remark wrings an involuntary smile from Rosa. "My brother told me you were an awful strange cop," she says.

31

The assistant caretaker at the reservoir walks along the outer base of the dam, training a flashlight on the concrete. He spots a deep, long crack. Water emerges from it pulsingly. "Get the hell out of here!" he shouts to the men atop the dam. "It's breaking up."

32

Graff's vehicle reaches the wreckage of Wilson Plaza, where the Army Corps of Engineers has already begun rescue operations. Barbara, who left the building before its collapse, tells Graff that besides Remy and Sam Royce, Denise was inside. Graff speaks to the officer in charge of the project, the same colonel who earlier checked out the dam. "There's a chance people could be alive in the sub basements," the colonel admits, "but it'll take days to unearth all that debris. The air supply can't last more than a few hours."

"I've studied this building's design," Graff argues. "Been inside it hundreds of times. If the storm drain running past the basement is deep enough, all you have to tunnel through is a couple layers of concrete and a few feet of dirt!"

The colonel says that he has already sent a team down to examine the possibility of going in via the sewers. They have reported that the eastern approach is blocked, and the western end is choked with loose rubble. "Come on and see for yourselves," he says.

Graff, Slade, and the colonel descend a forty-foot steel manhole ladder into the storm drain. Workers are studying a collapsed section. The concrete overhead has buckled, forming a crooked arch. However, an opening exists through the debris, barely high and wide enough to accommodate a man on all fours.

"Trouble is we don't know how far it runs," the crew foreman says.

"You haven't checked?" Graff asks.

"Could cave in any second," the colonel says.

Without hesitation, Graff crawls into the gap. With every moment, dust and loose chunks of concrete come down on him. Frightening groans go through the rubble. But, fighting panic every inch of the way, he continues.

Slade and the others wait tensely. Minutes later, Graff reappears. "I got through!" he cries. "Find me a jackhammer, a light—"

"None of my men are going in there, and you can't handle a job like that alone," the foreman says.

"Won't be alone." Smiling tightly, Graff jerks his thumb at Slade. "He's coming with me."

Slade gives Graff a tired, fatalistic nod.

The rescue crew runs a power line down the manhole, provides Graff and Slade with a jackhammer. They drag the hammer through the opening in the rubble, begin drilling into the drain wall. "We ought to come out in the basement's third level," Graff predicts.

At the first blast of the jackhammer, chunks of loose concrete fall. The work crew on the far side of the barrier frantically scrambles up the ladder to the street. On the surface, the colonel is told that the Hollywood dam is in danger of breaking. "I want an immediate report on any changes in it," he tells his radio operator. The colonel knows that although the streets around Wilson Plaza are on high ground, the deep storm drains will flood within minutes if the dam collapses.

After more than an hour's work, Graff and Slade drill a hole through the basement wall, discover that more than seventy people are alive in the garage. They widen the gap, enter. Denise rushes into Graff's arms. Remy, further back in the crowd of survivors, instantly realizes that the girl must be Denise Marshall. Hurt and angry, she steps forward, is recognized by Graff.

However, there is no time for quarreling. Graff and Slade hastily organize the evacuation. Corry—strapped to his stretcher—is carried out first by the medics, followed by most of the women.

33

Another aftershock strikes. Everyone freezes until the tremor passes. They have no way of knowing that the mild quake has been the ultimate blow to the Hollywood dam. The concrete breaks with an overwhelming roar, releasing a tremendous wall of water.

Homes are smashed into wooden shreds, hundreds swept to their deaths as the flood strikes Hollywood.

34

At Wilson Plaza, most of the trapped people have reached the clear section of storm drain. Corry has been hauled up the manhole shaft by the medics. Denise follows. Among the men and women waiting to ascend the ladder is Remy. Slade and Graff are the last to crawl through the tunnel in the debris.

They hear an ominous rumble. An instant later the storm drain fills with swift-running water, carrying off dozens. Remy is halfway up the ladder when a man steps on her hand. She loses her grip, plunges twenty feet into the drain. Graff and Slade, fighting the current, have almost reached the ladder. Graff sees Remy's thrashing body swirl past. He glances up the shaft, spots Denise far above. Everything in him wants to follow her. But he pushes himself away from the ladder, swims after his wife. He reaches Remy, struggles to keep her afloat. A section of the weakened drain roof gives way right over them. They disappear in the churning water.

Realizing that he can do nothing to help, Slade climbs to the surface. About twenty-five other people, including Dr. Vance, have made it to safety. Rosa breaks out of the crowd of spectators, hugs Slade with relief.

Denise walks quietly away, her eyes welling with tears.

Slade and Rosa gaze out over the devastated city. "Used to be one hell of a town, officer," Vance says numbly. Lew Slade nods, pulling Rosa closer.

Dozens of helicopters on rescue missions whirl through the darkness.

35

Distant sirens wail, and National Guard gunfire crackles, as Los Angeles burns on.

Charlton Heston, as Stewart Graff, an engineer, and Ava Gardner, as Remy, his wife.
Remy, with her father, Sam Royce (Lorne Greene).

The first quake strikes a downtown office building. Caught outside nearby, Graff and Remy take cover under a car.

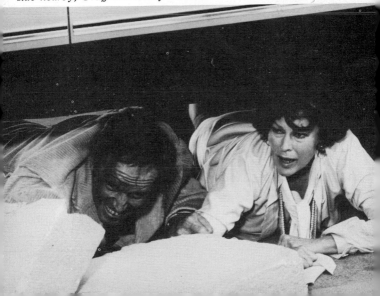

Rescuing the trapped office workers.

Just before the quake, Miles Quade (Richard Roundtree), dare-devil cyclist, and his assistant Sal (Gabriel Dell), practice their act.

he quake strikes and policeman Lew Slade (George Kennedy)
ies to keep order.

In different parts of L. A., Sal's sister Rosa (Victoria Principal) and Remy wander amid the devastation.

Denise Marshall (Genevieve Bujold), caught in the earthquake, goes to look for her son, Corry, and finds him in the paved bottom of a river runoff.

Jody (Marjoe Gortner) leads his National Guard squad, as Lev
Slade commandeers Graff's car.

Confrontation between the psychotic Jody, Slade, and Graff.
Below, Graff and Slade rescue the injured.

The second quake strikes the temporary hospital, catching Dr. Vance (Lloyd Nolan), Denise, and Corry.

Graff and Denise reunited at the shelter, but Remy seems trapped.

The final blow: the dam bursts and much of the shelter is flooded.

Graff and Remy are caught in the floodwaters; Rosa and Slade wait for the survivors.

Director Mark Robson and crew against the wreckage.

Setting up the action.

Robson directing the stars.

Rubble and wreckage, expertly faked.

Between shots, the cast rests, while technicians prepare for the mood.

EARTHQUAKE

The Background
and
The Making of the Movie

GENESIS
or
"You sure as hell <u>can</u> shoot it! I'll bet you could shoot it for forty million dollars!"

The top floor of Los Angeles police headquarters—one of the tallest buildings in the downtown area of America's most sprawling city—houses a cafeteria, servicing the hundreds of policemen and civilian employees who work below. On a warm afternoon in July, 1973, producer-director Mark Robson and I were having coffee with the detective sergeant who handles public relations for the department's emergency-control division. A graying, rugged-looking man in his forties, the sergeant was articulate, wryly charming, firm in manner—perfect casting for a modern TV-style cop.

We visited headquarters as part of our preliminary research on *Earthquake,* a film concerning the long-predicted major tremor that, many experts believe, is virtually certain to hit California within the next decade. A meticulous craftsman, Robson wanted a definitive briefing on the city government's plan to deal with the effects of such an awesome natural catastrophe. It had already dawned on both of us that quite possibly, there *was* no plan.

"We maintain constant liaison with the civil defense people," the sergeant said. "In an emergency, Marine and Coast Guard helicopters can be put at our immediate disposal. And, of course, there's the National Guard to protect property and serve as auxiliary forces for the police."

67

Like his previous statements, it sounded suspiciously generalized. Earlier we had toured the department's emergency-control center on a lower floor. The large, plain room was filled with row after row of long tables, each with dozens of telephones on it. During city-wide emergencies, the phones would be manned by specially trained officers, in contact with police substations throughout the vast city. The sergeant had told us how well this communications nerve center had worked during the violent racial disturbances in Watts and other past local troubles.

"Sergeant, I've been wondering something," I said. "Your center depends primarily on telephones. That'd be fine in case of rioting, even huge fires, maybe. Still, some seismologists are expecting a quake of at least eight points on the Richter scale. A shock that big would almost certainly knock out electricity and phones in most of the city."

"That's a problem," the sergeant admitted. "We lost some phone communication for hours during the Sylmar quake in seventy-one. The ideal situation would be to have radio consoles, powered by emergency generators, at key points."

We asked other questions. Since the construction of skyscrapers in an earthquake zone has been greeted with dismay by most seismologists, wasn't the city setting a poor example by putting up towering buildings like police headquarters? Had any studies been made on how long it would take to evacuate dangerous areas, such as those in the floodpath of the Hollywood Reservoir dam? The replies were inconclusive.

At last the sergeant acknowledged that the city lacked a master plan dealing specifically with the ravages of a monstrous earthquake. "The central problem is simply this—we've never had a really massive quake in Los Angeles," he said. "So we lack hard data on what the results would be. You can't draw up a plan unless you know what you're planning *for.*"

I suddenly relaxed. Ever since signing to work on the screenplay of *Earthquake,* I had been a little nervous about my qualifications for the job. (These doubts were, of course, kept from my employers). I was primarily a comic writer, had always steadfastly avoided epic subjects. Now—assured by the sergeant that the L.A.P.D. would be fully prepared for the *second* time the city was totally destroyed—I knew how to handle the script. I was on safe ground, the edge of the absurd.

First approached on *Earthquake* more than six months earlier, I had yet to hit a typewriter key. I had the same agent as Mario Puzo, who, more than a year before, had written a first draft screenplay dealing with the anticipated California catastrophe. Tied down to a contract for a sequel to *The Godfather*, he felt that he couldn't simultaneously handle two jobs of that size. He and the agent suggested to Jennings Lang, Universal Studios executive producer for the film, that I continue the project.

"I'll be in New York next week," Lang—whom I had never met—told me over the phone from L.A. "My secretary has already mailed you the Puzo script. Read it and then we'll talk." (I live in New York, as does Puzo. To this day, I don't have the vaguest idea why no California writers were considered for a story rooted so deeply in the physical and social nature of the state. Actually, in retrospect, I feel that my initial ignorance may have helped the picture, since I was unable to fall back on the kind of local source material that fails to travel. I vividly recall seeing Woody Allen's *Bananas* in a Madison, Wisconsin, theater several years ago, laughing like hell amid an otherwise silent audience. At least half the jokes were comprehensible only to Caucasians residing between 79th and 103rd Streets on the Upper West Side of Manhattan.)

Originally, I expected to put in from six to eight weeks of rewrite time, unaware that it would be more than a year before the words *final script* appeared on a title page. I was halfway through reading the Mario Puzo screenplay when I realized that the job—if I got it—might prove more difficult than anticipated. Long before the unprecedented success of *The Godfather*—both book and film—I had considered Puzo to be among the finest American novelists, one of the few whose stylistic talents matched his story-telling sense. The screenplay of *Earthquake* reflected his phenomenal gifts. It had brilliantly drawn characters, was packed with exciting events and telling, ironic insights. Unfortunately, there was no practical way that I could see in which many of the principal scenes—dealing with the great quake and its aftermath—could be photographed!

Example: At a key point in the original story, the heroine—Denise Marshall—is driving along a crowded freeway. It buckles and collapses, causing hundreds of car wrecks, mass chaos. Thrilling stuff, but today's sophisticated audiences wouldn't accept the scene if process photography and other obvious special effect tricks were used. It would look incredibly phony. The only alternative would be to actually wreck a freeway. Besides being economically unfeasible, this might lead to friction with the city government.

Scene after scene had such problems. And the non-disaster events were so closely linked to the key quake incidents that each "impossible" shot knocked out a dozen others that, under other circumstances, would be usable. In short, "rewriting" virtually meant starting all over again, finding a way to fuse Puzo's best concepts into a workable cinematic structure.

On a cold morning late in January, 1973, I kept an appointment with Jennings Lang at the MCA building on Park Avenue, easily the most un-"show-biz" offices of any entertainment corporation on earth. Furnished with antiques, hunting prints mounted on the dark, wood-paneled walls, the place resembles an interlocked series of bank board rooms. Lang, a tall, craggy-faced man with a rumbling voice, fit his surroundings. He had a curiously nineteenth-century manner. I easily imagined him, with correct costuming, as a member of Grover Cleveland's cabinet. Secretary of the Interior, maybe. (Actually, this turned out to be a false impression. I soon discovered that Lang possessed a wild, often unsettling sense of humor. He wouldn't have lasted thirty days with Cleveland.)

Our first conversation got off to a not uncommon start. Lang subtly let it be known that he had never heard of me. (One of the most charming and least re-marked-upon qualities of famed film producers is their willingness to hire writers they've never heard of. They assume, I suppose, that writers they've never heard of work cheaper. They are right.)

Formalities out of the way, Lang propped his feet on the edge of his somber, deep-grained desk and filled me in on the history-up-to-now of *Earthquake:*

"You remember *Airport?* Biggest hit Universal ever had. A couple of years ago, I was running it with Lew Wasserman. He's the MCA chairman of the board. All of a sudden, watching the picture, it occurred to me that in just about every disaster movie you had a bunch of people getting on a boat or a plane. *Airport, Posei-don Adventure, High and the Mighty,* damned near all of them. But millions of men and women hardly ever get on boats or planes. What about a picture where the common disaster comes to *them,* instead of the other way around? Let's get *that* audience! An earthquake seemed the natural thing, at least if you live in Califor-nia ... So I went to work, hired Mario Puzo to come up with a story. You read the script?"

I nodded.

"What'd you think?"

"It's great on paper," I said, "but I don't see how you can shoot it."

Lang sat upright, glared at me indignantly. "You sure as hell *can* shoot it!"

"Oh?"

Grover Cleveland's Secretary of the Interior van-ished. "I'll bet you could shoot it for forty million dol-lars!" said Lang, releasing a raucous, the-world-is-going-mad-all-around-me laugh at his exaggerated statement of a nonetheless real problem.

We spent the next two hours spitballing ideas about turning out an earthquake movie that wouldn't bankrupt the studio. I won't go into specifics since not one of these brilliant notions ever showed up in the film itself. "Well, I guess you see the problem," Lang finally said with a weary shrug. "I'll be in touch."

I'll be in touch are, needless to say, ominous words for a writer. Although, for pure discouragement, I doubt that I'll ever top an encounter with Otto Preminger in the winter of 1971. I had been out all day, returned home in the evening to be told by my wife that Preminger's office had called. Assuming it was about a job, she had made an appointment for me to meet him the following afternoon. That night a merciless snowstorm fell on the city, continued all the next day. But naturally I kept the appointment, arriving at Preminger's office in a semifrozen state. He sat behind a desk the size of an aircraft carrier's flight deck, waved me to a chair opposite him. On the desk was a copy of a screenplay I had done for a New York producer a few months earlier. I don't know how—or why—Preminger got hold of a copy. "This is very interesting material," he said, "However, there are a few things about the script that need work." For the next half hour, he tore the story to pieces, pinpointing error after error. "Well," he said in conclusion, "I just thought you'd like my opinion. I try to help out young writers whenever I can." Although gratified to learn of this unpublicized altruistic streak in the director's nature, I nevertheless felt an odd depression as, teeth chattering, I trudged through mounting drifts toward the subway station.

Anyway, I'd long since learned that film assignments can vanish like ice cream spilled on a hot sidewalk, deliberately suppressed enthusiasm until the papers were signed and the first check had cleared the bank. In this case, it wasn't easy. I had found *Earthquake* genuinely exciting as a subject and knew that, considering the trend of the industry toward "smaller" topics, future chances to work on a movie of such overwhelming scope might be few.

It was late in February before I heard from Steve Sheppard, my agent, on the project. I had already decided that either Jennings Lang had hired another writer, or the studio had dropped the picture. Then the phone rang. "I think you've got the job," Sheppard said. "They've signed Mark Robson to produce and direct. He's going to be in town for the next couple of days. If he okays you, you're in."

I had lunch with Robson, he *did* okay me, and a few days later the Writers Guild of America went out on strike against the major Hollywood movie studios.

RESEARCH AND DEVELOPMENT
or
"No matter how you slice it, there's no way to take a moral position against earthquakes."

Living on the East Coast and belonging to a West Coast union is, even in good times, annoying. You're always receiving invitations to attend great-sounding film retrospectives you can't possibly get to, being asked to vote for guild officers you've never met or expect to meet. During a strike—and this was my first—the situation is heightened to occasional surrealism. In the months that followed, my mail box was stuffed daily with all kinds of union literature. The most frequent were form notices to report for picket duty in front of 20th Century Fox or Warners or Universal. I naturally felt that the cost of plane tickets would put too great a strain on my financial resources, even when I started getting mimeographed postcards about the gloomy fate awaiting members who continued to ignore picket notices.

Until the last minute, nearly everyone I knew had assumed the strike wouldn't come off. When it did, the equally confident prediction was that it couldn't last more than a week or two. (It ran for sixteen bitter weeks and by the end had spawned a few thousand grimly funny stories. My favorite was told to me by an agent friend. "You can't imagine the phone calls I'm getting," he said in mildly stunned disbelief. "There was this producer yesterday. He asked me to convince a writer to finish a script he started before the strike.

'You have my word of honor that this matter will be held in the strictest confidence,' he told me. Then he rattled off the names of half a dozen other writers who were *already* scabbing for his company!"

One advantage for an Eastern writer is that in periods of trouble he isn't pinned down to a single industry. I picked up a few magazine assignments, tossed away my mimeographed warnings, and continued more or less normally. The only hitch was that I had become hooked on *Earthquake*. Before the strike I had bought a stack of reference volumes. Now, even though I had no guarantee that the job would even exist by the time the walkout ended (no contracts had been prepared, much less signed), I found myself reading them at odd moments.

Although there were no scientific studies of quakes before the eighteenth century, they have been a scourge of man throughout history. Aristotle and Seneca wrote about them in ancient times. The earliest known report of cataclysm was a tremor off the coast of Greece in 425 B.C., so severe that it tore away a huge chunk of the land, creating the island of Euboaea. In the year 17 A.D., another destroyed the city of Ephesus in Asia Minor. Constantinople has the uneviable honor of having been leveled twice, in 557 and 936. A quake is even recorded in the Bible. "The mountains skipped like rams and the little hills like lambs," reads Psalm 114. "Tremble thou earth, at the presence of the Lord, at the presence of the God of Jacob; which turned the rock into a standing water, the flint into a fountain of waters."

The ancients' explanations were often fanciful. The Algonquin Indians believed the earth rested on the shell of a giant turtle, and quakes hit when the world shifted on its back. In other areas, primitive tribesmen thought the earth was supported by an equally huge hedgehog. A tremor occurred whenever the beast stopped to scratch itself against a tree trunk. More "rational" men had other theories, just as unlikely. Thales, the Greek philosopher, thought the world floated on water and quakes struck when storms roiled the waves. How else, he asked, could you account for the new springs that often spurted out of the ground after earthquakes? Aristotle proposed that tremors were the result of winds being forced into great caverns beneath the ground, where they whipped around trying to get loose. When the pressure below grew too great, the earth's crust was ripped asunder. His evidence was that before most quakes the air grew stale and motionless. This theory was accepted for nearly 2000 years by many scholars.

Modern times have also had their share of cataclysms. The Kansu, China, quake of 1920 took more than 200,000 lives. Three years later, one of the most severe earthquakes ever recorded struck Tokyo, killing more than 150,000. *Mosaic,* the magazine of the National Science Foundation, estimates that

seventy four million persons have died as a result of earthquakes. Just in the second quarter of this century, three hundred and fifty thousand have died. It would appear that the United States has been extraordinarily lucky so far. Less than twelve hundred have died in American earthquakes even though the United States has had several great earthquakes. The biggest occurred in the nineteenth century when the local population was dispersed and great modern ones have taken place in as yet sparsely populated parts of the country. But it is clear that someday—perhaps soon—the relentlessly increasing population curve and the earthquake curve will cross.

The U.S. casualty figure in the *Mosaic* article startled me. It seemed almost ridiculously low. I had seen news film of the devastating 1964 quake in Anchorage, Alaska, where ships had turned over in the harbor, streets ripped up for hundreds of yards, houses crushed like paper cups in a child's fist. Still photos of the great

San Francisco quake of 1906 had shown scenes of unrelieved destruction, as if the city had been hit by modern aerial bombs. Amazingly, I now read, little more than 500 people had died in the latter tremor, many of them actually killed in the huge fire that followed it. The Anchorage catastrophe had taken only an estimated 100 lives. Other quakes over the years—beginning with the Charleston, S.C., temblor of 1886—accounted for the rest of the fatalities.

Only 1,200 out of 75,000,000, I thought, wondering if this incredible run of luck had contributed to Californians' heralded indifference to their looming fate.

I soon had the chance to learn in person. On June 24, the Writers Guide settled its dispute with the studios. The next morning, I got a phone call from Mark Robson, asking me to fly out to the West Coast as soon as possible. I left on the twenty-sixth.

I had been a Mark Robson fan years before I'd ever heard of him, from the day I scared myself silly at a Boris Karloff film called *Isle of the Dead*, one of the director's first pictures. Toward the end of the film, a woman in a cataleptic trance is sealed in a coffin. She comes to and lets out a yell that sent me and every other kid in the Rahway, N.J., theater crawling into our popcorn boxes.

A veteran of almost thirty years in the industry, Robson—born in Montreal—came to the Los Angeles area as a teen-ager, studied law at U.C.L.A., dropped out when an assistant cutter's job opened at RKO studios. "It was in the height of the depression," he told me somberly while in a reminiscent mood. "Work was scarce in this business." "You must have had it rough," I replied. "Of course not!" he said, beaming triumphantly. "My father was rich. Matter of fact, I had the family chauffeur drop me off a couple of blocks from the studio every morning so nobody'd find out. If they had, they'd have given my job to someone who needed it." (Like any first-rate director, Robson obviously knew how to lead his audience into a trap.)

Robson worked as a film editor through the early forties, became one of the best in a demanding trade. With Robert Wise, he cut the Orson Welles' classics *Citizen Kane* and *The Magnificent Ambersons*, most of the other top RKO pictures of the day. Both men moved up to director's status with the late Val Lewton's justly famous low-budget horror-film unit, working as directors or editors on *The Cat People, The Seventh Victim, Bedlam, Isle of the Dead,* half a dozen other offbeat chillers still beloved by movie buffs. (While we were working on *Earthquake,* Robson was interviewed by the very young editor of a film-art magazine. "He wasn't interested in anything after the Val Lewton days," the dumbfounded Robson said later. "Kind of a shock to learn my career was over before I thought I'd started it!")

In the late forties, he hit the Hollywood big time with a medium-budget adaptation of Ring Lardner's short story *Champion,* considered by many critics to be the best boxing picture ever produced. The sleeper, which made Kirk Douglas a star, was an enormous box-office hit, earned Robson raves for his hard-hitting, realistic, marvelously energetic direction. He followed it up with *Home of the Brave,* the first Hollywood film to deal seriously with antiblack discrimination. Later successes included *The Bridges at Toko-Ri, The Harder They Fall, Von Ryan's Express, The Inn of the Sixth Happiness, Nine Hours to Rama, Valley of the Dolls, Peyton Place,* and *The Prize.*

In short, it wasn't like going to work for Gerard Damiano.

Along with Bernard Donnenfeld, James Bridges, and his old friend, Robert Wise, Robson is a partner in the Filmakers Group, an independent production outfit with offices in a nondescript gray bungalow on the Universal lot. Suffering badly from jet lag—I suffered from jet lag when planes still had propellers—I showed up at Robson's office around ten. Robson had already been at work since 6:00 A.M. I soon learned that he habitually rose before dawn, conditioned by years of early shooting on weekdays and a bizarre urge to be first to tee off at his golf club on weekends. (This was to be the only strain in our relationship, since I do my best work between midnight and 4:00 A.M. Some days we saw each other just long enough for me to groggily hand him a few pages of script and then stagger back to my hotel.)

A stocky man with a mischievous, rather knowing smile, Robson asked his secretary, Cecile Kramer, to make some coffee. Then he got down to business. "George," he said, "before we do anything, we have to decide what this picture is going to be *about*."

I had been dreading that question. I have never met a writer with talent who gave the faintest damn what a story—in any medium—is "about." They usually figure that if the characters and incidents are dramatically valid, the underlying theme will emerge naturally from the material. That doesn't stop film directors, producers, book and magazine editors from asking. On the other hand, writers seldom have to face the people who put up the millions of dollars necessary to make a high-quality motion picture. Those guys *really* want to know what a story is about!

"Oh, well, it doesn't matter that much right now," Robson said calmly after I'd uttered a string of lame generalizations. "We have a lot to do before you really get down to work. I'm certain something will occur to you."

For the next two weeks, I was almost constantly in Robson's company—and sure enough, by the end of our research period I knew what *Earthquake* was going to be about. For the first few days we drove around Los Angeles. Possibly Robson's guided tour was deliberately calculated to emphasize the characteristic. Maybe not. In either case, I gradually developed the impression of a community unconsciously dedicated to a state of endless peril.

Our first stop was the Hollywood reservoir dam, high in the hills above the film capitol. We first looked at it from the freeway below, not that there was anything much to view except a forest of dark green pines climbing a steep slope. "They planted the trees years ago," Robson explained as our car climbed a narrow road. "When I was a kid, you could see it plain as day. Then the area started building up, and I suppose the real-estate people figured a big white dam overhead wasn't much of a selling point. So the city put in the woods to hide it. I'll bet not one person out of ten even knows it exists."

We rounded a steep turn, and the reservoir—a large body of green water backed up behind a broad concrete dam—lay below. Built in 1929, its façade was covered with rather charming Romanesque sculptures set in deep niches. A representative of the L.A. Water and Power Department was waiting for us at a gate in the wire fence surrounding the reservoir.

"You people aren't going to break the dam or anything, are you?" he asked a little nervously as he showed us around. (The city gave full cooperation to the making of *Earthquake*, but understandably, officials were cautious about the film's overall image of their policies.)

"I really don't know," Robson replied truthfully. "We haven't written the script yet. Just checking it out."

After inspecting the dam, we drove even higher into the hills. It was an area of wealthy homes set on huge lots. Obviously, one of the area's attractions to the rich had to be the reservoir, spread out below like a vast private lake. Beyond, obscured by comparatively mild smog, lay all of Hollywood—first, neighborhoods of small private houses, giving way to the high office buildings near the intersection of Vine Street and Sunset Boulevard. Even larger, newer structures could be made out in the distance.

"Hell of a flood path, isn't it?" Robson said with a chuckle.

"Pretty good."

"This view is one of the reasons I decided to do the picture," he said. "Jennings asked me once before, more than a year ago. I read the first script, decided it was too scattered. Hardly any of the people knew each other. The action took place all over Los Angeles, from Malibu to downtown. Nothing to bring it together. Then I remembered the dam, how from here you saw just about every type of building and neighborhood imaginable. So I brought Bernie Donnenfeld up, and I said to him: 'This is the way. Give the characters some shared, unifying danger beyond the quake itself. Something hanging over their heads, rich and poor alike.' "

I was, at first, dubious, but kept my reservations to myself. "Waiting for the dam to bust" seemed to smack of nineteenth-century stage melodrama. If you were going to do it, I felt, you needed to do it in a way no one else ever had, introduce an element of total surprise for the audience. (Incidentally, I was right. The looming menace of the dam proved to be the second toughest element in writing the screenplay. The image of a stereotyped "good guy" yelling, "Run for the hills! The dam is gonna bust!" danced before my eyes every time I started a scene involving the reservoir. Since I abhor false modesty, I'd like to state that, in my view, the problem was solved handsomely. But I'll go into that later.)

"A couple of years ago—after the Van Norman dam nearly collapsed in the Sylmar quake—there was talk about draining the Hollywood reservoir," Robson said thoughtfully, gazing downward. "Just as a precaution. Nothing ever came of it. The way I heard, some of the people who live up here managed to block any action. They said that draining the reservoir would wreck the view, lower the value of their property. Of course, they're on high ground . . ."

In the following weeks, I came to realize that Mark Robson and *Earthquake* were a perfect match-up of director and subject. He had lived in Los Angeles almost since childhood, had gone to school here, married and raised a family here. His daughters and grandchildren had been born—and still reside—here.

To me—at least in the early stages of the film—L.A.

was a place I visited when my employment called for it. Everything except my hotel and the studios where I briefly worked remained essentially abstract, a tenuous background to my personal and professional concerns. I feel the same thing is true for many movie people who maintain homes in Los Angeles. Their roots are elsewhere. Substitute a house for a hotel, and their situation is little different from my own. But Robson loves the town, has an emotional stake in its past and its future. The fact shows in every frame of the completed film. He knew—and understood—what he was wrecking.

Another stop on our tour was Pacific Palisades, an area of towering—and crumbling—seaside cliffs. Like potential suicides teetering on a twentieth-floor ledge large homes sat atop them. The splintered ends of fences, torn off during earth slides, jutted seven or eight feet into empty space. Many of the houses backed right up on the chasm, would obviously plunge to destruction even in a mild avalanche.

We drove to the top of the cliff, cruised slowly past the fronts of the homes. Some were empty. Others had FOR SALE signs posted on the front lawns. Incredibly, to me, we saw a moving van pulled up in a driveway, and workmen were carrying furniture *into* the house!

"This is a lovely neighborhood," Robson said. "A few years ago, some of these places had backyards a hundred feet deep. Then the slides started. But people still live here, as you see. The best part is that some oil company wants to drill wells on the beach below the palisades. Engineers say the drilling will drain off ground water and increase the erosion even more. The city still hasn't made up its mind whether or not to give them permission!"

We went on to Coldwater Canyon, where families had deliberately built their homes veering off into space. Everywhere you looked were stilt houses erected on steep hilltops, their rear decks supported by heavy steel girders. "These things are popping up all over the place," Robson explained. "Damned if I know why they build them. The view, I suppose. How'd you like to see a few come crashing down?"

"I have a feeling we will," I replied wryly.

On my own, I explored Topanga canyon, northwest of the city, one of the scariest-looking areas in L.A. A two-lane blacktop road winds along the bottom of the canyon, which has nearly vertical walls in places. It is like a catalogue of past disasters. For miles, trees are black and gnarled from the roaring fires that sweep through parts of the area during the dry season; the ground around them, a dark-gray stubble of dead brush. During the rainy months, massive mud slides are equally common, burying homes, cars, and people beneath tons of earth. But hundreds of houses were visible on either side of the road, their occupants undauntedly defying the odds on destruction.

Another day, Robson and I drove to the downtown business district. The last time I had been there was as a teen-ager, on vacation in the early fifties. Then, most of the area had been filled with older, wooden homes—on the verge of dilapidation—ringing out from a few office buildings, few more than ten or twelve floors high. Now most of this was gone, replaced by modern skyscrapers like Richfield Towers. Dozens of others were being erected everywhere. It was like a shining-new Manhattan.

"What do the experts say on those?" I asked Robson.

"Nothing much good," Robson replied flatly.

We had a scheduled meeting in L.A. City Hall with a representative of the building department, a cheerful, heavyset man in shirt sleeves. His desk was cluttered with blueprints and drawings. "Sure economics have a lot to do with it," he said. "How couldn't they? It's easy to say 'Tear everything down and start over,' but where does the money come from?"

Asked what type of building would be the most dangerous in the case of a major quake in the Los Angeles area, he shrugged and said: "The older ones, put up before the new regulations came in. Actually, we aren't too worried about private homes. Though, naturally, we've upgraded specifications there, too. Statistics show that the greatest loss of life occurs in heavily built-up areas. The safest structures of all would be massive buildings—you know, telephone centers, power plants, places deliberately built to protect and maintain heavy electrical equipment. They can take almost anything."

"Unfortunately, few people live in power plants," I commented with an involuntary grin. "Mark and I were looking over some of the skyscrapers downtown. How safe are they?"

"As safe as we can make them. The hitch, of course, is that no one really knows what will happen to a modern high-rise in a big quake. They've never been tested. Critics talk about upgrading building codes, but to a professional that doesn't mean a hell of a lot. Building codes are *averages* based on what punishment structures have withstood in the past. And frankly, even top engineers aren't sure which is the correct approach to building earthquake-resistant structures."

He took up a pencil and a pad of paper, drew a crude high-rise, marked out heavy subterranean pilings. "Some think this is the way—pure strength and rigidity. It has its advantages in that all the quake stress is put on the building's frame. This minimizes possible loss of life and property destruction *inside*. But in the case of a prolonged, steady quake the whole thing might come down."

Another few slashes of the pencil produced a second high-rise. Next to it, he drew the same building, twisted into an S shape. "Another approach gaining favor is to make the structure as flexible as possible. In layman's language, that means the high-rise absorbs the energy of the tremor, rides with it. A forty-story building put up with a flexible design would literally crack like a whip in a big quake. As the energy comes up through the frame, the top floors would move several feet, snap back in place like a rubber band when the tremor passes. You can imagine what happens inside. Desks and chairs and other office equipment—to say nothing of people—would be thrown all over the place. It's pretty certain you'd get greater human injury—at first, anyway—than with a rigid structure. The advantage is that a flexible building can take far more frame stress, would remain basically intact where a rigid one would be reduced to a mountain of rubble. It's six of one and half a dozen of the other. Just how big a quake are you fellows figuring on?"

"At least nine points on the Richter scale," I said.

"The biggest ever," Robson added.

The building-department spokesman laughed and shook his head. "Can't give you any help there, I'm afraid. No one on earth knows what'd happen with a shock like that. All bets would be off."

Later, studying books on the earthquake danger in California (by far the best is *Life Along the San Andreas Fault* by John J. Fried, Saturday Review Press, 1973), I found more frightening facts on the susceptibility of modern buildings to quake damage. Some of the most hard-hit structures in the San Fernando Valley tremor of February 9, 1971, were recently erected, or still under construction!

Killing 64 people, racking up more than half a billion dollars in property damage, the so-called Sylmar quake hit at 5:59 A.M. As tremors go, it was moderate—6.4 on the Richter scale. For the first time Californians saw what could happen when a comparatively mild quake hits in a heavily built-up area. Nearly 825 homes, 65 apartment structures, and 574 commercial buildings—most built in recent years—were destroyed.

Among the hardest hit was Olive View hospital. Built in 1970 at a cost of $27 million, it was wrecked beyond repair. The phenomenal "good luck streak" running through the history of U.S. quakes held once again. More than 600 persons—patients and staff—were in the hospital at the time. Only four died—two of injuries, two when electrical failure cut off their respirators. However, fatalities could have been far greater. According to the California Institute of Technology's report, the severely damaged columns supporting the structure could never have stood up to five more seconds of strong ground shaking.

Luckily, fire did not break out, since all four of the hospital's emergency escape towers collapsed. Like the building itself, the towers were constructed with "quake resistant" techniques. So was a $45 million water-treatment plant, half completed. It suffered $6 million worth of damage. Other almost-new buildings wrecked were a $110 million converter station and the San Fernando juvenile detention center, damaged beyond repair.

Since the Sylmar quake was the most recent in the L.A. area, involved the same kind of modern buildings that would be affected by a bigger shock, what happened there in 1971 inevitably became the research "scale model" for the vast cataclysm depicted in *Earthquake*.

The last person interviewed by Mark Robson and myself was Dr. Clarence Allen, director of seismology at the California Institute of Technology. With the possible exception of the legendary Dr. Charles Richter—now semiretired—Allen is the top man in his profession. We had a lunch appointment with him at Caltech's faculty club. "Isn't this a great old building?" Robson asked me as we entered the club's main salon, a magnificent, wood-paneled room with towering ceilings. "How'd you like to have a roof like that come down around your ears?"

(I had already become used to Robson's growing affection for the chaos ahead. We had visited City Hall, the planetarium, the international restaurant at Los Angeles airport, many other landmarks, all examined for their potentiality as spectacular debris. It got to be kind of fun.)

Dr. Allen was a tall, lean, suntanned man in his early forties. Wearing boots and a Western-style checked shirt, he looked more like a prosperous farmer than one of the world's most renowned scientists. His unaffected, almost diffident manner threw me off my stride as an interviewer. And Robson's, too, I suspect.

Although Universal had not yet given a go-ahead on actual production of *Earthquake,* I knew that Robson had already been casting roles in his mind, working from characters in Mario Puzo's original story. Among them was a world-famous seismologist—elderly and bootless. I knew how Mark felt. Nothing is harder to accept than a neat preconception undermined by reality.

During the lunch, Dr. Allen patiently filled us in on the origin, effect, and history of California earthquakes. He confirmed that in his view, the proposed film's prediction of a major quake along the San Andreas fault theoretically was valid. Virtually the entire Pacific coast of the Western Hemisphere rests on a series of geological faults. Simply put, "faults" are vast adjoining sections of the planet's surface moved by natural forces in opposite directions. In many cases, this gradual shift—often several feet a year in some areas—is harmless. Trouble comes at points where the earth's crust locks in place and compresses—as in the Los Angeles-San Francisco apexes of the San Andreas. Eventually, this stored seismic power must be released—with catastrophic results on the surface, miles above.

However, it was while discussing the human effects of a big quake that Dr. Allen really shook us. No one else we had spoken to—private experts or government officials—had mentioned the hopelessness of current plans to deal with a massive quake.

In Puzo's story, the state attempted to organize a mass evacuation of Los Angeles when seismologists predicted an upcoming disaster. Granting that a prediction system would eventually be developed, Dr. Allen was pessimistic about the possibility of evacuation. "How?" he asked rhetorically. "It might take weeks to get millions of people out, with no guarantee that the place they're evacuated to is any safer than the city. Mass panic would be inevitable. More might die in the evacuation than in the quake . . . It would be wiser to send people to their homes, clear out tall buildings, close schools . . ."

From my viewpoint, the most important preliminary research on the film came "after hours," talking to friends and acquaintances who had lived in Southern California for years. In *Life Along the San Andreas Fault,* John J. Fried writes: "Probably not one Californian in a million gives more than a passing thought to earthquake faults and earthquakes. In New York, muggings are reported to the press every day. Partygoers regale each other every day with tales of raped ond robbed friends. There are daily reminders that life and safety are tenuous commodities. But in California, earthquakes just do not strike every day. When they do, to be sure, the results are devastating, and the reminder is immediate. But as the aftershocks fade and weaken, as the mess is cleaned up and pushed out of the way, the reminder of danger goes with them."

Fried goes on to quote a housewife from a San Francisco suburb. Her home sits virtually on the San Andreas fault. "We are not worrisome people," she told him. "You can look into the fault from the upstairs window. But then if you worry, you don't live anyplace. We just wanted a place where we could live and which we could afford. After looking at a hundred houses, you don't worry about earthquakes, anymore."

Superficially, I felt that Fried is right. Californians *have* shoved their never-ending peril into the backs of their minds. However, I'm not certain how far back. I noticed that as soon as anyone learned the name of our proposed movie, they came up with vivid recollections of quake experiences, either personal or second hand. Inevitably, these revelations ended with the equivalent of the words: "But what the hell are you going to do about it?" Nevertheless, the awareness of danger is an ingrained part of Californians' lives.

Naturally, those involved in the production of *Earthquake* had their tremor stories to tell. Back in New York, Jennings Lang had remarked that the jolt of the Sylmar quake had been one of the main spurs to his development of the project. "My wife and I were just about knocked out of bed," he said. "The whole house was shaking, and we were miles from where it happened. I'd like to say we did all the smart things you're supposed to do in quakes, but we didn't. I ran into my teen-aged son's bedroom, and he wasn't there! So I rushed downstairs, yelling his name. Then all of a sudden I hear *him* yelling to me: 'Dad, you dope! Get under a table or something!' There he was, crouched under the archway to the dining room. I was just starting to crawl under the dining room table when the shock passed. Struck me kind of funny later. The same thing must have happened all over the city—kids remembering the survival rules they'd been taught in school, adults crashing around like nuts."

Charlton Heston, who plays the starring role of Stewart Graff, remembered the '71 quake far more calmly, probably because he lives high in the hills, in an area of solid, ancient rock formations. Seismologists know that quakes are felt more strongly in low-lying, loosely earthed areas. In the 1906 San Francisco disaster, the worst damage was in working-class neighborhoods, built on what had once been bay mud flats. The wealthy homes on Nob Hill were untouched. However, several burned down in the great fire that followed, striking a blow for economic equality.

"I was just getting up when the Sylmar quake hit," Heston recalled, "and it certainly got my attention, I can tell you that. We all got up and the power went off and the phones shortly went out, which was the case all over town. There was no damage in our house aside from some hairline cracks and some concrete decking.

"The swimming pool had white caps on it, but it wasn't a profoundly traumatic experience. If I had lived out on the fault, where houses were turned over, I suppose I might have reacted differently . . . We were working on a film so I proceeded to the studio early, as is my custom, to get sone work done before the phones started ringing. I planned to write some letters, but the electric typewriters didn't work. Then I thought 'I have some scripts I should read,' and it was winter and dark and the lights weren't on, so I couldn't read. And I said

I'd better phone my mother and tell her everything's okay. But the phones weren't working. It was a very quiet morning for me . . ."

Victoria Principal, the lovely young actress who portrays Rosa Amici, reacted far less calmly to the Sylmar quake. "I was in the hospital," she told an interviewer. "The TV set flew off the wall and shattered at the end of the bed. I was scared to death. I remember the hospital bed, which was on springs, bounced around like a pogo stick. I thought someone's dead spirit had come back to get me. So when the nurse said it was an earthquake, I was relieved that the devil had not come back to take possession of my soul . . .

"My fright was excessive but after that even a mild shock will make me nervous all day. When nature goes on a rampage, you have a complete feeling of helplessness. Everyone in the world can say 'let's stop it,' but it won't do any good . . ."

Her trepidation was justified, but not because of any satanic menace. On the record, hospitals are just about the worst place to be in a quake. Besides the Olive View Hospital, the Sylmar shock destroyed or did serious damage to the San Fernando Veterans Administration Hospital, Indian Hills Medical Center, Pacoima Lutheran Hospital, Holy Cross Hospital, and the Kaiser Memorial Hospital.

The collapse of the V.A. hospital had a sidelight that may or may not give comfort to the religious, but certainly illustrates the capriciousness of a tremor. Although the main building was devastated, a tiny interdenominational chapel on the grounds was absolutely untouched. "There is an eerie sense of peace and quiet inside the small stucco building, which stands out amid the rubble," reported the *Los Angeles Times* the following day. "A small sign outside the door reads 'Enter, rest and pray.' Eight stained-glass windows, which line the sides of the chapel, were not even cracked when the earth beneath the hospital began to shake, collapsing two buildings and claiming the lives of at least thirty-nine patients and employees. The windows tell the story of Christ . . ."

George Kennedy ("Lew Slade" in the film) has gone through many quakes. His recollection of the Sylmar tremor was typical: "I woke up, and my daughter was halfway through the house! My son got out of bed and was walking around. He had his eyes open but was still asleep. I grabbed both of them and put them into my bedroom. There were a number of aftershocks, and we just automatically came to that room. It was scary . . .

"That was the first one we'd been in together. My wife had been in one years before, and I had been in about nine of them, mostly in Japan, where they have a lot of earthquakes. But the ninth is just as scary as the first one . . .

"You know, I fly airplanes and people say, 'Aren't you afraid to fly?' I always answer that there's some legitimacy to the airplane. You have trouble, and there's some chance of making a landing. You're in control. But in an earthquake, you have a feeling of helplessness. Where are you going to hide? At least I do, and it bothers me . . ."

Lorne Green ("Sam Royce") went off on a more philosophical tack after seeing a rough cut of the film: "It'll frighten the hell out of them, that's for sure. I'm thinking of buying a hundred thousand acres up in British Columbia so that all of the Californians will have a place to run after it comes out . . . You know, man has never been able to stand against nature. I think that's when we first got religion. You know, 'Protect me against this. Help me with my crops. Bring me rain. Protect me against earthquakes and tornadoes and volcanoes and everything else.'

"Look at all the tornadoes we've been having in the Midwest. It's something that suddenly hits, and there's no forewarning. In the picture we see this. Of course, there's been a great deal of scientific work in predicting earthquakes, and we've brought this out. But even with a prediction, what do you do? That's the big question still to be answered."

Most of the above remarks were made with a press agent at the speaker's elbow. The most honest reaction to my questions came from a barmaid at the Sheraton-Universal hotel where I stayed while writing the script. "You're doing a movie on earthquakes?" she gasped. "*California* Earthquakes?"

"Well, yeah."

"You're crazy! Who wants to be reminded about earthquakes? Every time we have one—I don't know why but I always hide in the bathroom—I promise myself never, *never* to think about earthquakes again! And I never do. When is the movie coming out?"

One of the most annoying—professionally—aspects of my research was that I'd never felt an earth tremor myself, even though I'd once lived in Mexico City, one of the world's most quake-prone cities. I was always out of town when they hit, a bit of luck that most people might envy. So everything I had learned remained curiously abstract.

At the end of our research program, Mark Robson and I returned to Universal Studios for a conference— over a bottle of Scotch. We were joined by Bernard Donnenfeld, president of the Filmakers Group. Donnenfeld is a tall, shy man with a constant expression of patient resignation. *No one I come into contact with in this business is ever going to behave reasonably,* his manner seems to say, *but I've learned to live with it.*

"Well, are you fellows ready to go to work?" he asked.

"Almost," Robson replied cheerfully, then turned to me. "George, have you figured out what this picture's going to be about?"

"Yeah," I said. "It's going to be about what people think they are and what they *really* are."

I don't imagine it was the answer he'd expected. For one thing, it had nothing to do with earthquakes. But Robson accepted my remark with an understanding nod. "You know, I'm starting to feel good about this one," he said thoughtfully. "It's going to b a lot more than just a thriller. I think we have an opportunity to make a real statement about the world we live in."

Donnenfeld—one of whose chief functions is to constantly remind his high-powered creative partners that after all Filmakers was a profit-oriented concern—reacted to this warily. From the beginning of his career, a deep vein of social concern had run through Robson's films. "Okay, Mark, but don't get carried away," he said. "Just keep in mind that we're after the biggest, most exciting action picture we can come up with."

"Bernie has a point," I added, not quite facetiously. "No matter how you slice it, there's no way to take a moral position against earthquakes."

"It'll *be* the biggest, most exciting action picture we can come up with," Robson promised. "But at the same time we'll let the audience know about some of the crazy things going on all around us. The way I figure it, we're obligated to."

(Donnenfeld's worries proved to be ill-founded. The finished film of *Earthquake* must be the least preachy motion picture on a serious subject ever made. Charlton Heston—playing a construction engineer—has one or two brief scenes where he mentions how quake damage could be modified with better building-design techniques, and that's it. Any further overt comment proved unnecessary. Action tells everything.)

After Donnenfeld left I made myself another drink. I was returning to my chair when suddenly the rug under my feet seemed to move with a lurch. My left shoulder jerked to the right; my feet, to the left. The ice rattled in my glass, and liquid ran out, trickled down my sleeve. For an instant, I felt suspended in midair.

"You know what that was?" Robson asked gleefully.

"An earthquake?" Only now had fear come, a tiny spurt of fear, like the hard-edged splash of a dental Waterpik, deep inside me.

"You better believe it!" Robson said.

THE FIRST-DRAFT
SCREENPLAY
or
"Okay, I'll tell you what I think. I...hate...it!"

As people who write articles like this reiterate at tiresome length, movies are a collaborative art. *Earthquake,* was in some ways, more collaborative than most. Quite frankly, I really didn't know what I was doing. All of my earlier scripts involved half a dozen characters in simple dramatic situations. They had required no special knowledge of the technical side of film making beyond an understanding of terms like *cut, fade, dissolve to,* etc. Anyone even halfway bright can learn that stuff in twenty minutes.

Earthquake was another matter entirely. The effectiveness of the big quake scene and the rescue-and-escape action sequences that followed required an encyclopedic knowledge of movie technique, everything from the handling of miniatures to "blueback photography." (I'm still not sure what the latter is and it was explained to me half a dozen times.) And I had the lesson of Mario Puzo's original story to demonstrate what could happen when a writer didn't fully understand the medium's limitations.

Since I was too old to enroll in the UCLA film school—and the first draft was due in eight weeks, anyway—I put it to Mark Robson squarely: "I think we ought to work on the quake sequence together. It'll be a waste of your time and mine if I churn out a bunch of copy that you won't be able to shoot."

"Haven't you learned anything about this business?" he asked teasingly. "A writer is supposed to exude absolute confidence at all times."

"Oh, screw it," I replied.

But the quake scene was weeks away. First came the step sequence—a scene-by-scene outline of the picture's principal action. Before even that began, we spent several days discussing our overall approach to the script. We had already agreed on one thing—that we didn't want *Earthquake* to be like any other disaster movie ever made.

In my New York meeting with Jennings Lang, he had continually held up *Airport* as a model for the new picture. Since coming to California, I had slowly come to realize that beyond using an all-star cast and concentrating on action and suspense, *Earthquake* had to take off on a new path. "You know something," I told Robson, to emphasize my point. "I've never really liked disaster movies except for *King Kong*."

"It's too late to throw in a giant monkey," he said with a sigh.

"I mean it. I can't think of a single picture about a disaster that was completely satisfying. Or a novel, either—even a so-called classic like *Bridge of San Luis Rey*. Always something lacking."

"What?"

I had thought out my answer before I knew the question would be asked. At Robson's urging, I had gone to see *The Poseidon Adventure*. I had been avoiding the film on purpose. Since I was working on a screenplay involving disaster, I didn't want to be influenced by another story in the same genre. (Not all writers are so admirably scrupulous in these matters.) I watched the movie with mixed reactions. The special effects and adventure scenes (the tidal wave, turning over of the ocean liner, underwater swimming, et al.) were even better than the reviews had indicated. But if the characters stopped to talk, the picture went dead. God knows their backgrounds were interesting enough, and the dialogue wasn't bad, but for me ennui settled in whenever the physical action temporarily halted. Of course, I'd had the same reaction from just about every other picture of the type I'd seen in recent years.

"You know what bothered me?" I said to Robson. "There was no dramatic connection between Hackman's and Borgnine's and Stella Stevens's lives and the capsizing of the liner. You could have yanked out the principal characters and dropped in a dozen other people with different backgrounds. It was all chance, random."

"*The Poseidon Adventure* grossed one hundred forty million dollars."

"Don't be picky."

"Well, if you're right, how do you beat it?" Robson asked.

"By making damned sure our leads are in trouble, or at least tense as hell, from the moment we first see them. No fat, contented Jewish grandmothers taking presents to the kids in Israel. No happy honeymooners flying off to Hawaii, and the plane's wings fall off. None of that crap. An earthquake is a release of seismic energy. Our people ought to be as pent-up and ready for release as the ground under their feet. Without slamming them over the head with the fact, we ought to make the audience feel—unconsciously, in their nerve ends—that the quake is somehow generated by the characters they're watching, not the San Andreas fault alone."

"That's a pretty tough order."

"We can but try," I said with a shrug, surprised at my own bombast.

(Actually, I think the completed film comes pretty close to achieving the desired effect. Stewart Graff, the male lead, is on the edge of leaving his wife after years of unhappy marriage, learns facts about her on the morning of the quake that bring him closer to a final break. Remy, the wife, is struggling to hold on to him at whatever cost. Sam Royce, her father, discovers the situation, is torn with indecision about how to handle it. Denise Marshall, a young widow in love with Graff, senses the conflict within him, is uncertain about continuing their relationship. Lew Slade, the cop, has been suspended from the force, is taut with rage over what he considers an injustice. On a lighter note, Miles Quade ["Gino Amici" in the first draft], the daredevil motorcyclist, is preparing to audition an insanely dangerous stunt for a Las Vegas promoter, isn't sure he can bring it off. Rosa, a girl who helps Miles in his act, is worried sick that he will kill himself. Dr. Willis Stockle and Walt Russell, the seismologists, have predicted a major earthquake within forty-eight hours, are desperately attempting to convince officials that the danger is real. All of their problems reach the boiling point at the exact instant the cataclysm hits.)

There was a second reason why, in my view, it would be impossible to imitate *Airport* or *The Poseidon Adventure*: the very nature of an earthquake. In most stories of shared peril, the characters are trapped in a place from which they cannot escape: the passenger cabin of a plane, the interior of a ship, a sealed-off mine tunnel. There was an easy way to do this, of course. Our leads could be in a hotel, for example, when the quake strikes, buried alive in the basement. The rest of the film would then deal with their efforts to escape. Robson and I agreed that this approach would be a subtle cheat. The very title *Earthquake* promised scope and movement, a vast stage for the action.

The next problem, therefore, was to tie our people together without jamming them into an enclosed area. We spent more than a week on the step sequence, meshing the characters in a plot scheme that, without sacrificing credibility or overdoing coincidence, would leave audiences with an integrated, unscattered story. (Again, I feel we succeeded, though, of course, the final verdict would come at the hands of the public.)

Only one loose end remained after the step sequence was complete: the fate of the Hollywood Reservoir dam. "We've implied over and over again that the dam is in terrible danger," I told Robson when we reached the key earthquake scenes in the tentative outline. "The audience will be all keyed up, expecting it to go with a bang."

"And?"

"It won't go."

"That, my boy, is what is known in the trade as an anticlimax," Robson said. "Will it *ever* go?"

"I'm not sure," I said. "For the time being, maybe we should leave that part of the step sequence blank."

"I really don't see where we have any choice." Mark Robson, as I have mentioned, is a very patient man. "Oh, one other thing. I gave my word to Jennings that every incident in the quake scenes will be authentic. If it isn't based on a real happening in the past, at least we ought to make certain it's possible. One fake bit can make more trouble for a picture than you can imagine."

(I think that *Earthquake* achieved its goal in this respect. Every moment of fictional destruction was checked out for what someone—I forget who—called "the reality quotient." So, too, were the psychological reactions of crowds and individuals to an earthquake's havoc.)

It was the middle of July before a word of my first-draft screenplay appeared on paper, nearly seven months after my New York interview with Jennings Lang. Since coming to California, I had seen Lang only twice, both on social occasions. The antithesis of the legendary interfering executive producer, he had scrupulously kept out of Robson's and my way, would continue to do so until we had finished the first draft.

Not that he wasn't busy enough. Besides producing theatrical films, Lang once ran Universal's program of made-for-TV movies, the most extensive put out by a Hollywood studio. He had practically invented the form back in the early sixties. ("In those days, the networks were down on dramatic anthology programs," he told me. "Playhouse 90, stuff like that. All gone. I was an MCA agent then. Anyway, I went to the network brass with a package of ninety-minute shows. They almost threw me out the door. 'Plays are poison,' they said.

'Who's talking about plays?' I asked. 'These are *movies!*' That one word—*movie*—sold them.")

The Writers Guild strike had created a huge production backlog on the Universal lot. Every foot of office space was in use as companies struggled to make up for lost time. So the first draft of *Earthquake* was written in a room in the Universal-Sheraton hotel on a steep hill overlooking the lot. (Robson at one point considered knocking it over, later decided this might not be the best idea that had ever hit him.) I soon found that I wasn't alone. The hotel cocktail lounge was full of harried-looking men with scripts under their arms.

The plight of a writer hunched over a typewriter in a hotel room for weeks is essentially undramatic. Dissolve too:

Mark Robson's office on the Universal lot, mid-August. Robson had just read my first draft and liked it except for the inevitable problems. I've been asked how difficult it was to write the major quake scenes for the film. Hardly anyone believes that this was the easiest part of the job. Research and Robson's technical expertise made the task, on paper, a cinch. The disaster sequences in the finished film vary only in minor details from the first (of ten) screenplays. Even the nagging problem of the dam had been basically resolved. I had decided to hold off its collapse until the final moments of the picture, when the audience thought everything that could possibly happen to the people in the story *had* happened. Stretching one suspense element through more than two hours of film—without straining the viewer's patience—was accomplished by tying in virtually everything that happened on the dam with the central story (the Graffs live in the hills above it; Denise is almost killed when the dam-inspection team releases water to relieve pressure; scientists in the seismology lab are puzzled by the strange, accidental drowning of the reservoir caretaker, etc.). This sounds simple, but many of the brief, almost throwaway scenes at the dam were eventually rewritten as often as twenty times to achieve the desired effect.

Our primary problem was harder to solve. Put bluntly, the hero, Stewart Graff, turned out to be a jerk. In Mario Puzo's story, the most important character was Denise Marshall, a divorcee having an affair with Graff, a rich married businessman. Puzo's Graff seemed to have been intentionally made hypocritical, so indecisive that when forced to choose between his wife and Denise, he commits suicide! I had retained the triangle but tried to transform Graff, turn him into a rugged, determined construction engineer. Instead of being the passive figure of the story, he took charge of rescue operations after the quake, performed heroically throughout. In the end of the first draft, he and Denise survive the flood in the storm sewer. Remy, his wife, is killed after unsuccessfully trying to murder Denise in a jealous fury.

"Graff is *still* a jerk," Robson declared after reading the script.

"I was hoping you wouldn't notice."

Why Graff was still a jerk remained a mystery for months. Theoretically, a writer—at least in a commercial medium—should be able to make a character as attractive or unattractive as he pleases. Why not? "All you have to do is run it through the typewriter again," say nonwriters. It's never been true. Often, characters defy revision. The harder—as in this case—I worked to make Graff sympathetic, the less sympathetic he became. It was baffling and infuriating.

Obviously, Robson and I agreed, I had overlooked a simple but crucial element in the man's nature. But since Robson didn't know what it was, either, we decided to let it ride for a while.

Oddly, at the first-draft stage, no one worried about this except Mark and myself. Others who read the script—including Jennings Lang, Bernard Donnenfeld, and Sid Sheinberg, the president of MCA—seemed to find Stewart Graff to be a perfectly acceptable hero. They made incisive, valid criticisms on other aspects of the screenplay, but Graff didn't bug them. At times I thought Robson and I were suffering a shared hallucination, but not often. Something *was* badly wrong. Weeks were wasted on rewrites of the scenes in which he appeared. And nothing helped. The answer came after the screenplay was supposed to be finished—out of nowhere, during a telephone call! And that's how you end up doing ten drafts.

Before sending the script in to be multilithed, Robson decided to bounce it off Jennings Lang. He had kept his distance all this time, but signs of strain were showing. "I ran into Jennings at the commissary yesterday," Robson said. "He's getting nervous."

The rough draft was delivered to Lang, and the following day Robson and I had a long story conference with him, the first of many. Lang, I soon realized, had a disconcerting way of approaching a script. He would ignore all the big points and zero in, like an ICBM programmed to nuke a henhouse, on some minor imperfection. It took days or even weeks for me to realize that by the time I'd fixed the minor imperfection, whole sections of the screenplay had been changed along the way. It's quite a gift!

"These people are boobs!" he growled, opening the script.

"All of them?" I asked, startled.

"No. Robby and Susan."

Robby and Susan were a young married couple, neighbors of Denise Marshall. Robby was, in the first draft (and no others), the graduate assistant in seismology who first figures out that a quake is about to level Los Angeles. Susan, at home when the tremor hits, was the original victim of Jody, the supermarket clerk's rape attempt.

Lang had numerous other improvements in mind, but Robby and Susan were his major gripe. Since they weren't very important to the story, Robson and I casually promised to eliminate them. (To tell the truth, they *were* kind of insipid, stock juveniles.)

That promise led to a major change in the story—for the better. Getting rid of Robby was a cinch. An hour's work metamorphosed him into Walt Russell, the dedicated—and unmarried—seismologist of the completed film. Susan presented a more serious problem. "Jody is one of our best characters," Robson said, "and the rape scene is really necessary. We can't have him rape a total stranger!"

"Happens all the time."

"Not in this picture."

The solution was to expand the role of Rosa Amici, at first the sister (later, just good friends) of our daredevil motorcyclist. The cycle sequences were conceived as a crazy, funny, running counterpoint to the more serious sections of the film. Determined to perform the most perilous motorcycle stunt of all time, the daredevil and his mechanic erect a lunatic network of loop-the-loops, ramps, fiery hoops, et al. Just as he is about to start his run, the big quake knocks the whole rig flat. Rosa was, basically, an onlooker.

In the rewriting, we had Rosa leave the field before the demonstration starts. She is in a movie theater when the tremor comes, is left alone afterward to find her way home, is mistakenly arrested for looting by the National Guard, is "rescued" by Jody, on duty as a guard sergeant ... One damn thing followed another. By the time the second draft was completed, Rose was a romantic interest for Lew Slade, the suspended cop. From a near walk-on, she had become almost as important to the story as Remy and Denise!

"Heaven help us if Jennings ever wants a *big* change!" I told Robson after we realized what we had wrought.

(In future conferences, I grew to respect Lang's frankness in dealing with a script, though it occasionally reached the abrasive stage. One of the most annoying aspects of dealing with many producers is their unwillingness to tell you what they really think. You can be nine-tenths finished with a screenplay before it suddenly hits you that the guy loathes everything you've done. By that time he has secretly hired another writer to carry on, and you're out of a job—never really knowing why. Lang's reactions were immediate and unequivocal. He reached his finest hour when, somewhere around the eighth draft of *Earthquake,* he was presented with a minor change in a lead part. The actor signed for the role had decided his character wasn't deep enough, thought it needed an extra dimension. So, experimentally, I gave him a phobia—fear of enclosed places. Since he had to crawl through a collapsed storm sewer, this was a remarkably inconvenient phobia. "Tell me what you think, Jennings," I said to Lang during a meeting. "Okay, I'll tell you what I think," he said grimly after reading the new material. *"I . . . hate . . . it!"* Rough on the ego, but by God you knew where you stood! Besides, he was right.)

I made some additional revisions after further conferences with Lang, and the amended script went to Sid Sheinberg. Since the first—and possibly only—phase of my contract ended with the second draft, I caught a plane for New York, still not sure that *Earthquake* would ever be made. (I'm not certain when the decision came to proceed with the picture. Maybe never. I have a director friend who swears he has several times gone from development into full production without getting the official word from anybody. "I have a recurring nightmare," he said. "I've just put an eleven-and-a-half-million-dollar super-spectacular in the can, and an executive comes up to me and asks: 'Who the hell told you to do *that?* '")

I had been home less than a week when I got a phone call from Mark Robson. "Come on back," he said. "Sheinberg has okayed the script but . . ."

"He wants some changes," I said.

"How'd you guess?"

CASTING
or
"Doesn't want to change her image! What image? She hasn't worked in five years!"

I know film writers who have almost gone into shock when the roles they've created are "miscast." I used to sympathize with them until I witnessed the agonies Jennings Lang and Mark Robson went through in lining up the all-star cast of *Earthquake*.

While writing the third-draft screenplay, I finally had an office on the lot—rather, borrowed the office of director Don Siegel, who was shooting a picture in London. If Siegel should read this, I'd like him to know that I'm the one who drank the eighty-seven bottles of Fresca in his refrigerator. I'd hate to see a secretary get the blame.

One afternoon I dropped in on Robson, who sat with Bernard Donnenfeld, frowning over a long typewritten list. "What are you guys so gloomy about?" I asked.

"We're going to start casting," Robson groaned.

"What's so bad about that? I read that the Screen Actors Guide has a ninety percent unemployment rate. They'll be standing in line."

Donnenfeld gave me a pitying glance. "You've never been around when a picture was cast, have you?"

"No."

"I didn't think so. It's hell, especially when you're doing an action picture."

"Actors hate action pictures," Robson explained. "They want to do 'drama.' "

104

" 'Drama' is when the camera remains stationary for twenty minutes and the actor gets to recite a speech on the rights of man," Donnenfeld cut in. "Actors have an instinctive loathing for movement in any form."

Robson's method of casting was to prepare a list of all performers who might conceivably fit a role. Most are soon crossed off, chiefly because phone calls to their agents disclosed that they had conflicting assignments during *Earthquake*'s shooting schedule, tentatively slated to begin on February 11, 1974.

Topping the list was the part of Stewart Graff. Besides Charlton Heston (who, of course, eventually played the role), it included Paul Newman, Steve McQueen, Burt Reynolds, and Jon Voight, among others. "Always the same people," Robson remarked. "I think Paul and McQueen are tied up, but it can't hurt to give them a call. I like to talk to actors personally, sound them out on a role."

"Isn't Voight kind of young for Graff?" I asked.

"You can always rewrite," Robson said with a small, wicked smile.

For the part of Remy, Jennings Lang wanted Ava Gardner. The legendary star now lived in London, worked only occasionally. Lang planned to fly over and personally discuss the role with her. Robson had directed Gardner in *The Little Hut* years before. "She takes a long time to make up her mind," he remarked. "And is pretty good at changing it after she has! I'm at least going to talk to other actresses."

"And she might not want to do the part," Donnenfeld added. "I personally think she'd be great, but it's kind of out of her line."

I realized what he meant. In every Ava Gardner film I'd seen in years, she had played roles that can only be described as "beautiful and stately," moving through them perfectly gowned, every hair in place, ravishing but—frankly—a little dull. Except for a few brief scenes in the beginning of the film, the part of Remy is gruelingly physical. She is pelted with debris, shoved under a truck, buried alive in a basement, forced to crawl on her hands and knees through a collapsing sewer, finally drowned in a swirling flood of water. It was highly unlikely that an actress could manage all that and keep every hair in place.

(Robson proved to be right. Ava Gardner told Lang that she wanted to think it over. At one point—weeks later—it looked almost certain that she would turn down the role. In the meantime, Robson had interviewed several actresses he thought might be right for Remy. It was decided to make a firm offer to one of them, known in the fifties and sixties for playing sweet, beguiling, understanding, upper-middle-class women. Her feature-film career had recently been inactive.

("You know why I want her?" Robson said. "That perfect WASP wife quality. It's a great mask for bitchery. The audience will get a jolt when they realize the truth."

(To the astonishment of everyone, the actress turned down the part, stating that she didn't want to change her image. "Doesn't want to change her image!" Bernard Donnenfeld gasped when he heard the news. "What image? She hasn't worked in five years!")

Day after day, while supervising the film's pre-production schedule, Robson squeezed in dozens of meetings with actors' agents, saw performers almost every evening. I sat in on several of these sessions. A few times the situation was clear-cut. For example, James Stewart, approached on the phone for the role of Sam Royce, simply said that he didn't feel like working at the moment. More often—even in the case of minor stars either past the peak of their careers or still short of it—the agents stalled, citing conflicting jobs that "were just about to come through," always, naturally, at astronomic salaries.

After nearly thirty years as a producer-director, Robson was used to the game, never showed a trace of irritation. The closest he came to expressing annoyance followed a meeting with representatives of Joe Namath. He had wanted the football star for the role of the daredevil motorcyclist (back when he was still named

Gino Amici). While a basically peripheral character, it was—we both felt—a charming, flashy, funny role, one of the best in the film.

"We don't feel it's right for Joe," one of the representatives told him. "He did one of those Hell's Angels pictures before. You know, him and the bike carrying the whole thing. We're not sure we want him to play a hood again."

I grew mildly angry when Robson repeated the remark—not at the gentleman's statements, which would have been reasonable under other circumstances. What bugged me was that he obviously couldn't have read the script.

"Namath wouldn't be carrying the picture," I said. "It's a supporting role—strong but still supporting. And Gino isn't a Hell's Angel. He's a trick cyclist, an entertainer."

The week before, Robson had screened reels from some of Namath's earlier films. The pictures were silly, amateurish junk, thrown together solely to exploit the athlete's fame. However, Namath himself had been oddly extraordinary. He came across as a truly likable, unaffected, natural slob. I don't mean that as a knock. Skilled actors like Anthony Quinn have spent decades trying to come across as truly likable, unaffected, natural slobs. You aren't fooled for an instant. The "spontaneous" laugh always lasts a few seconds too long. The swagger is a shade overdone. Namath managed the style without even trying. He obviously had a real future as a screen personality, given decent roles in nonripoff films. That such a role should be rejected because the character owned a motorcycle struck me as awesomely weird. But then lots of things do.

Although Namath's people left an opening for future discussion, I sensed that Robson had written him off as Gino. Other actors were considered and rejected. Theoretically, it should have been an easy part to cast. What, after all, was required except charm and a strong physical presence? Plenty. The character had few dialogue scenes, had to establish immediate rapport with the audience. Actors who could manage it were rare.

Rosa Amici was another role that, a few months earlier, I would have said could be filled in two hours. Again, not so. Rosa was an eighteen or nineteen-year-old Italian-American girl, very beautiful, superficially hip—in actuality, rather innocent. I figured hundreds of young actresses could fill the part.

"Twenty years ago the big studios trained kids, kept them under contract," Robson told me. "Even ten years ago, outfits like American-International made those dumb beach-party pictures, other things with young casts. The kids were there. But today it's almost impossible to find an actress with any kind of talent who can pass for nineteen. Check the casting directories if you don't believe me. They just aren't there."

This point was driven home many weeks later, after Charlton Heston signed to play Stewart Graff. During a story conference in Robson's office, Mark happened to mention that Rosa still hadn't been cast. Heston nodded and, while idly studying his script, remarked: "Oh, they're out there, all right. Living in crummy furnished rooms all over town. The problem is—how do you locate them?"

Robson's gaze briefly met mine, a slight smile tugging at the corners of his mouth. I could tell that exactly the same thought had flashed through our minds. "Heston, you are tall, ridiculously handsome, one of the most famous movie stars in the whole wide world," I had wanted to say. "If *you* can't find a beautiful nineteen-year-old brunette in Hollywood, how in the name of God are *we* supposed to?" I didn't say it, though.

During the search for Rosa, we ran clips of various young actresses. One of them, from a made-for-TV film, featured Victoria Principal. She looked like the Rosa of my imagination—dark haired, softly lovely. But she gave an inert performance, smiling vacantly as she delivered her lines. (However, they were the kind of lines that called for a vacant smile, if only as an alternative to horrified disbelief.)

"She *looks* like the girl," I said.

Robson shrugged. "Rosa has to be full of vitality. This kid is listless."

On some key roles, decisions are deliberately postponed. Lew Slade, the suspended cop, was actually as important a figure as Stewart Graff. The two men never meet until the final twenty minutes, but they dominate the two main story lines, which build toward their eventual confrontation. The actors had to be perfectly matched. If one was too much stronger than the other, the remainder of the film could be fatally thrown off balance.

Jennings Lang and Robson decided that Graff should be cast first. Names were tossed about for the Slade role, but a final choice was momentarily out of the question. Actors considered ranged from Beau Bridges (ruled out because of his youth) to Alan Alda. ("He doesn't look like a cop, and that can be good," Robson commented. "And he has an offbeat, wild quality that would be fine for the part.") Jennings Lang's personal nomination was George Kennedy, but there was some doubt—genuine in this case—about his availability. He had previously signed to do a TV film at the studio, as well as a reprise in *Airport 1975* of his role in the first *Airport* film. However, Robson thought that by juggling the shooting schedule, it might be possible to use him.

Just about every prominent actress between the ages of twenty-five and thirty-five was considered for the key role of Denise Marshall—Jacqueline Bissett, Candice Bergen, Jennifer O'Neill, a dozen others. Again, except for general talks with agents, a decision was held off until we knew who would play Graff, to be sure the pair would make convincing lovers. (Strangely, in the early casting meetings I attended, the name of Genevieve Bujold—who ultimately played Denise—didn't come up once, probably because we all unconsciously associated her with classic parts like Cassandra in *The Trojan Women* or historical romances like *Anne of the Thousand Days*. Denise was her first Hollywood role, after years of working in Europe and her native Canada.)

For Jody, Robson wanted an actor with a boyish, middle-American face but with an underlying tenseness that would make his ultimate explosive violence credible. I suggested Tommy Smothers, the comedian and folk singer. Years ago, I had interviewed him in connection with a magazine article. Offstage his "underlying tenseness"—never utilized dramatically—makes a violin string look like a piece of overcooked macaroni.

However, Robson and Lang didn't want too many performers with strong television associations in the public mind. Although he had not yet accepted, Lorne Greene had been approached for the part of Sam Royce, Graff's father-in-law. As the long-time star of *Bonanza*, Greene would singlehandedly fulfill the picture's quota of TV personalities.

Robson proposed Michael J. Pollard for Jody, but he proved unavailable. Then Lang came up with an unusual suggestion—Marjoe Gortner, the former child evangelist. I had seen *Marjoe*, the documentary film on Gortner's abandoned religious career, agreed that he looked both middle-American and tense. Robson decided to interview him. He was currently in New York, wouldn't return to the coast for weeks.

Other parts remained unfilled because of disagreements over the nature of the character, even though I was only days away from completing the shooting script. One such dispute, strangely enough, involved politics. The new mayor of Los Angeles—Tom Bradley—was black, which created a dilemma. If we cast a black actor as our fictional mayor, everyone in the audience would assume he was supposed to represent Bradley. It would hardly be doing the mayor a service to suggest that during his administration the city was going to be flattened by an earthquake! On the other hand, if we used a white actor, it might be regarded as a statement of no confidence in Bradley's political future. (To many readers, this might seem silly.

They haven't read the mail studios get over such "minor" problems!)

While I was writing the first draft, Robson conceived what I considered a perfect solution. "The picture is set in the future," he said, "so basically we can do anything. Why not have a black woman mayor?" Thus, in the rough draft, Mayor Lewis was a lady. However, Jennings Lang objected. "We're after an international audience for this picture," he said. "Here in the States—with Women's Lib and all—everyone will understand what you've done. But what about the *macho* countries? Those people won't accept a woman as a figure of political authority. They'd be baffled."

In the end, Mayor Lewis—masculinity restored— was Caucasian and portrayed excellently by veteran actor John Randolph. Still, it hurt me to cut one line of dialogue during rewriting. "I used to think the two worst things that could happen to a person were being born black and female," the original mayor remarks after being told a major quake is on the way. "Then I had to go get elected mayor of Los Angeles!" I really missed that lady . . .

By the time I finished the shooting script in early December—still not satisfied with the character of Graff but admitting defeat—not a single leading role in *Earthquake* had been filled. However, Jennings Lang had scored a monumental casting coup—talking a powerful star into playing a part that didn't exist!

"I've just come from the advertising department, fellows," Lang said in his booming voice as he entered Mark Robson's office for a story conference. "They've dreamed up a tremendous slogan for the picture."

"Oh, really?" Robson said.

Lang spread his hands, indicating huge but invisible block letters. "How does this grab you? *Earthquake— The Biggest Disaster of All Time!*"

Robson managed a slightly strained smile. (He takes his work very seriously.) I roared. Lang is the only intentionally funny movie producer I've ever met; every outrageous remark is delivered with impeccable comic timing.

Lang turned toward me. "I have great news. Walter Matthau is willing to play the drunk. For the fun of it. No billing."

"What drunk?" I asked. Robson looked equally confused.

Lang opened the script. "It's right here. *A middle-aged drunk sits halfway down the bar.*"

"But, Jennings, that's all there is! The guy is a middle-aged drunk sitting halfway down the bar. He doesn't *do* anything."

Lang stiffened in outrage. "I convince a big star like Walter Matthau to play a part—for nothing—and you haven't given him anything to do?"

Stricken with guilt at having let down Matthau so badly, I promised to come up with something. (The result, in my view, is one of the comic highlights of the film. Throughout the scenes in the neighborhood bar where Lew Slade takes refuge after being suspended from the force, Matthau comments on the action by offering toasts to assorted celebrities. The effect is impossible to reproduce in type, so I won't try.)

By the middle of December—back home on Long Island—I figured that my work on *Earthquake* was done. After all, the last mutilithed script had carried the magic phrase *final screenplay.* I occasionally received telephone calls from Robson or Bernie Donnenfeld reporting that co-starring roles had been taken—Lloyd Nolan was to play Dr. James Vance; Barry Sullivan had signed as Willis Stockle; Marjoe Gortner would be Jody. But the major parts were still unfilled.

Just before Christmas, the phone rang again. It was Robson and Donnenfeld, on a conference line. They sounded uptight. "Maybe you can give us some suggestions," Robson said. "Charlton Heston is right on the verge of signing as Graff. He's the one we've wanted all along, but there's trouble. Minor points about the script bother him."

Robson read off the "minor points." They weren't

just minor, they were downright petty! The conversation implied that Heston was dissatisfied with some quality in the role, couldn't figure out what it was, and so nitpicked all along the line, a natural reaction. And suddenly I knew where I had gone wrong in developing Graff's character. In the early scenes, his actions had been insufferably smug. While criticizing Remy for her selfishness, he himself had been having an extramarital affair with Denise. It tainted him with hypocrisy throughout the remainder of the film.

"I think I know what's really bugging him," I said. "Suggest a change in the story line. In the new version, the affair with Denise will start on the day of the earthquake, after the fight with Remy. Up to then Graff has never touched her."

The statement was met by fifteen seconds of silence. "Okay, we'll try it," Donnenfeld said in a slow, dubious tone. "I guess there's no harm."

They called back less than an hour later, said that Heston had agreed to play Graff if the plot change was made. "It'll mean another big rewrite," Robson announced cheerfully. "But we're always glad to see you out here. No real hurry. A day or two after Christmas will be fine."

I flew to California for the fourth time, changed the script yet again. And almost miraculously Graff became fully alive, and fully sympathetic. At last, other big parts were being filled. Ava Gardner made up her mind to play Remy and Genevieve Bujold came in as Denise. George Kennedy signed as Lew Slade. The only roles still vacant were Gino Amici and his sister Rosa.

A few days after I arrived, Robson decided to view additional footage of Victoria Principal, on the chance that she hadn't been at her best in the TV movie we'd seen before. He chose reels from *The Life and Times of Judge Roy Bean,* her debut role as Paul Newman's Indian mistress. She *sounded* better—much more animated—but there was a hitch. We couldn't see her. *Judge Roy Bean* must have been the murkiest color film ever shot. Scene after scene was photographed in darkness or twilight or deep shadow. If the moon was right, you could tell that she had good teeth and the whites of her eyes were clear, but beyond that she was a blurred figure. *Everybody* was a blurred figure!

"Picture died," said a studio casting director sitting in on the screening.

Robson sighed deeply. "Well, make an appointment with her. We can at least talk. Oh, how's her figure? I couldn't tell."

"Fine," I said. "She did a layout for *Playboy* about a year ago."

Robson was delighted. "She *did!*" he exclaimed with a chuckle. "Nobody ever told me that!"

Victoria Principal eventually got the part, and under Robson's direction, showed the sexy pertness and vitality the role called for. Gino proved to be more difficult. Jennings Lang was determined to cast a big star. However, weeks after shooting started, the slot remained unfilled.

I had returned east yet again, after filing a script marked *second final screenplay*. (It came out of the multilith room as simply *final screenplay*.) There went the phone! "We have a problem," Jennings Lang said. "But first the *good* news. I'm after Richard Roundtree to play Gino. He's really hot for the part."

It seemed like a terrific idea. Roundtree—the young black actor who had reached stardom in the *Shaft* films—had the dash and charm and aura of strength needed for the role. Since the part didn't require any definite ethnic background, the racial conversion could be managed with a new name and minor dialogue changes.

Then it hit me.

"Jennings, you're already signed Victoria Principal to play Rosa," I said. "What audience anywhere in the world is going to believe Richard Roundtree has an Italian sister?"

"That's the problem."

It took less than a day to rewrite the motorcycle scenes. The solution—which had already occurred to

Lang—was to expand the character of Sal, the motor-cyclist's mechanic, an unimportant role heretofore. Gino became "Miles Quade," a black motorcycle dare-devil; Sal, amusingly played by Gabriel Dell, became Rosa's brother.

Earthquake was fully cast—nearly a month after the start of shooting. It had been one hell of a twisting road.

PRODUCTION

or
"Mark told me to order a flock of sheep so I did. Now this is my question. Where—in any script—does it mention a flock of sheep?"

Readying the physical details of a film as huge in scope as *Earthquake* takes months of work. The production office was set up in November, 1973, long before the cameras turned. In the beginning the only people working there were Robson; Wallace Worsley, the production manager; his secretary, Esther Panell; artists Leslie Thomas and Fred Tuch; and me. Don Siegel was due back from England, and I had been ejected from his bungalow. I moved into a production-office cubbyhole and continued writing. Fortunately, having started out as a newspaperman, chaos doesn't bother me that much.

All of Mark Robson's films are marked by economy of style and movement, a tough spareness. They look as if every shot, no matter how brief, has been thought out in advance. That's because every shot *is* thought out in advance. Thomas and Tuch had been at work for weeks when I moved in. Fred Tuch's job was to prepare detailed story boards, black and white panel drawings illustrating each scene. They would fill a dozen thick books before he was finished. Thomas concentrated on paintings of the more spectacular scenes, vividly colored representations of the action, defining the characters in relation to sets and actual locations.

Gradually other technical people set up shop, among them veteran art directors Alexander Golitzen and Preston Ames. They had last worked together on *Airport,* for which they received Academy Award nominations. Over the years, Golitzen has been nominated thirteen times, won three Oscars. Ames had a total of seven nominations and two Oscars.

For the film, Robson had asked Universal to hire two theoretically "retired" master craftsmen. One of them, special effects cinematographer Clifford Stine, was a much-heralded expert at photographing miniatures: scale-model buildings and vehicles, hundreds of which would be destroyed in the shooting of *Earthquake.*

Tall, laconic, the sixty-eight-year-old Stine had been living in Jackson, Mississippi, his wife's home town, when Robson called him. Stine had never really stopped working for long periods. For example, during a vacation in Spain, he had been recruited to handle the miniatures on *Patton.* (After *Earthquake,* he stayed on to shoot the tricky zeppelin sequences in *Hindenburg,* Filmakers' forthcoming thriller. At last report, he had sold his home in Jackson and returned to full-time Hollywood employment.)

"You have to keep one thing in mind," Robson once remarked to me. "There's hardly anybody left in the business who can do this stuff. For years, we've concentrated on ultra realistic stories, location shooting. The art of successful make-believe has been lost. Blowing up a four-feet-high model building and making it look absolutely real on film requires years of experience, a long history of trial and error. Now that big-scale entertainment pictures seem to be coming back, the Cliff Stines are at a premium."

He didn't have to convince me. I had two young children, had occasionally taken them to films like *Dr. Doolittle* and *Chitty-Chitty-Bang-Bang,* been appalled by the ineptitude of the special effects. So had the kids. When you can't fool a five-year-old, it's time to quit.

The second "retiree" was Dorothy Spencer, a gentle-mannered lady who has edited such distinguished pictures as the original John Ford production of *Stage-coach, The Snake Pit,* and *Decision Before Dawn.* This was her seventh film with Robson. "Dorothy's the best editor in America," he stated flatly. "And I'm going to need the best on this. Some of the big action scenes have nearly as many individual shots as whole films! And we'll be repeatedly cutting from full-size sets to miniatures. One mistake in matching up the action, even by a split second, can wreck an entire scene."

John Daheim, the stunt coordinator, also had a long association with Robson, dating all the way back to *Champion.* In that classic film, he had doubled as an actor, playing the middleweight champion defeated twice by Kirk Douglas. *Earthquake* would be the roughest job of his career, which has included staging dangerous action in such adventure spectaculars as *Spartacus* and *The Guns of Navarone.*

On this film, Daheim—a rugged-looking man with a dark, military-style moustache—would eventually supervise 141 stunt men and women. "Because of the unusual amount of dangerous action involved, this is the largest number of stunt people ever to work in a single picture, to my knowledge," he says.

Daheim began as a stunt man in 1937, doing wild tricks on a motorcycle in *I Like It That Way.* He had never ridden a motorcycle before. He took a bad fall, ended up in the hospital with huge chunks of skin ripped off his legs. "I was lying there in pain, and then I saw the paycheck," he recently recalled to a reporter. "It was six hundred dollars, and it was the middle of the Depression, and I was the son of a poor laborer. I realized then that I'd stay in the game.

"I went through the forties, fifties, and sixties. I did a picture called *Action in the North Atlantic,* in which I was blown up in a lifeboat, hurtled sixty feet in the air. In *The Racket* I was in a car that was hit by a train and turned upside down. I crawled from the car, jumped on the rear carriage of the train, shinnied up a metal ladder, and made it to the roof. In a push-button world, stuntmen are about the only adventurous men left. And if the end of the world comes tomorrow, who do you think would have the best chance of surviving it? The stuntmen would."

Involved in a less dangerous but equally exacting trade was Burton Miller, the film's costume designer. Ironically, few in the audience realized how much costuming was required. To casual eyes, it seems as though Charlton Heston and George Kennedy wear the same clothes throughout, since the action covers a fourteen-hour time period. Genevieve Bujold and Ava Gardner have a few more-obvious changes but not many.

"Dressing people for the quake was easy," Miller declared. "It was dressing them for the aftermath that was hard! When a person goes through a major disaster and ends up in a shambles, their costumes must go through many stages. The disintegration of the cloth must be believable. The clothing may age twenty years in one day . . .

"In the average picture, you may use two hundred pieces of wardrobe but in *Earthquake* we must have used over five thousand different garments for some one thousand actors, stunt people, and extras. We had to provide some of the stars with at least six different versions of each wardrobe change. Each change represented a different stage of action before, during and after the quake strikes and leaves the city in ruins.

"Ava Gardner was the best example. She wears a beige suit to meet her father at an elegant restaurant for lunch. Later she meets Heston, just before the big quake. They scramble under a car for safety as rubble showers down from buildings. When they come out, their clothing is soiled, and Ava's beautiful suit is actually torn. Later she's trapped by an aftershock in a basement, climbs through a dirty tunnel, and falls into a muddy storm drain with cold, rushing water. Each adventure had to be reflected in a corresponding costume disintegration. The same applied to all the actors . . ."

Wally Worsley, in charge of supervising physical aspects of the production, is a lean, elegantly dressed man with a gray, square-cut beard. He looks the way you might picture Captain Ahab before he got a little funny and started brooding about white whales. By the time I left the picture—just before major photography —a few pale leviathans were appearing on his personal horizon.

Repeatedly, as he tried to form a solid production schedule in the face of fearsome odds, he took me aside and asked pleadingly: "George, are we ever going to get a final script?"

"Christ, I hope so," I replied. "My wife is sending me poison-pen letters."

"I'm serious, George. There are things going on that you don't understand. Like the sheep. Mark told me to order a flock of sheep, so I did. Now this is my question. Where in any script does it mention a flock of sheep?"

He had me there. "You'd better ask Mark. All I know is what's in the script."

"I've tried to ask Mark, but I can't pin him down. I need help, George. *Scenes are scheduled that are not in any script!*"

At this point, late in January, Robson had become a human whirlwind, dashing from special-effects department to costumes to production office to every damned place you could conceive. He and Fred Tuch had even designed a car, the opulent four-wheel-drive vehicle driven throughout the picture by Charlton Heston. Basically, it was a stock Ford chassis, jazzed up at a cost of $5,000 with mag wheels, roll bars, a scarlet-and-silver passenger area, and about 200 pounds of chrome. Whenever it appeared on the lot, slavering car nuts desperately tried to learn where to buy one, refusing to believe the model didn't really exist.

Eventually, Worsley's problem was traced to Robson's penchant for improvising physical details within scenes. Instead of incorporating them into the script, he would have Fred Tuch and Leslie Thomas draw them into the story board sequences, base requests for items like sheep flocks on the drawings. By the time it was all straightened out, poor Wally was sharpening his harpoon.

Director of Photography Phil Lathrop reported for duty. A short, dapper man with an air of unshakable aplomb, Lathrop has shot more than fifty major motion pictures, including *Mame, Days of Wine and Roses, The Pink Panther,* and *The Americanization of Emily,* for which he received an Academy Award nomination. He and Robson immediately went to work developing entirely new techniques for depicting a giant earthquake.

A flaw in earlier films dealing with quakes was the uncertain relationship of the characters to the background action. Buildings would be crumbling all around them, but the people themselves remained relatively stationary, curiously unaffected by forces able to crack concrete. In reality, of course, they would be thrown about like poker dice in a cup.

Lathrop and Robson devised several original methods for heightening the realism of the quake scenes. One was the construction of a tremendous rocker platform on which such key sets as the neighborhood bar, Remy's bedroom, and Sam Royce's office were erected. The platform was in turn mounted on huge springs, attached to hydraulic rams controlled by variable motors. By changing the motor speed, studio technicians could program a tremor of any intensity they chose.

This method worked fine for interior sets. However, many scenes were to be shot on location in the streets of Los Angeles. You can't very well mount a city street on a rocker platform. To solve the problem, Lathrop and Universal's head machinist Louis Ami invented a special shaker mount for the camera. It is capable of both vertical and side motion, controlled by eccentric motors with rheostats attached to gauge the violence of the movement.

Without the camera mount, it would have been impossible to simulate seismological movements of stationery objects with such unbelievable reality. The instrument is demonstrated strikingly in several location scenes. In one, speeding cars careen out of control on an elevated freeway, which seems to quiver from shock after shock. A truck loaded with cattle roars through a guard rail into empty space. (A miniature truck takes over at the vital instant, but due to Dorothy Spencer's faultless editing, the switch isn't noticeable.) Actually, nothing is happening to the freeway. Undercranking the camera provided the illusion that the cars were moving at tremendous speed. Lathrop and Ami's camera mount did the rest. The same technique—combining a miniature and location photography—was used to film the collapse of the international restaurant at the L.A. airport.

Audiences gasp at a shot in the picture when an obviously real office building seems to bend, almost melt. While this kind of distortion effect is possible with a still camera, it was never achieved with motion-picture equipment before *Earthquake*. The shot resulted from an ingeniously simple trick devised by Mark Robson. Actually, the camera lens is never touched. The scene was photographed by reflecting the building in a sheet of flexible plastic mirror, bent by hand to create the necessary illusion.

The most publicized innovation in *Earthquake* has been "Sensurround," developed by O. W. Watson of Universal's sound department. The system had its germination, months before shooting, at a meeting held in Jennings Lang's office. While Robson and I looked on, Lang conferred with a group of technicians.

"For a picture to make it big these days, it has to be a real event," Lang said. "A *Badlands* or a *Mean Streets* gets terrific reviews, but nobody goes because they aren't events. There's nothing about them original enough to get the public out of the house. Our job is to make damn sure people know *Earthquake* is an event, that they'll see and hear something they've never seen or heard before."

For the next hour, the technicians presented all kinds of gimmicks. Some of them were, to put it kindly, wild—like bouncing huge chunks of styrofoam debris off the audience's heads during the tremor scenes. Other suggestions: Use live actors on stage during the disaster sequences, seemingly emerging from the screen carnage; develop slide-projection systems to flash vivid photos of quake destruction on the theater's side walls; install a mechanism on the projector that, during the cataclysms, would divert the image on screen to the walls and ceiling. Lang listened in silence.

"What'd you think of all that?" Robson asked as we walked back to work.

"Not a hell of a lot," I admitted. "Why spend seven and a half million dollars on a picture if you're going to show it on the ceiling?"

"Don't worry," Robson said. "Jennings will eventually shake it down to something fairly sensible."

The answer was "Sensurround." Put simply, the system is based on the fact that, below the 16-to-20 cycle range, most sound becomes inaudible to human ears, is sensed as pure vibration. In selected theaters, *Earthquake*'s print will hold a fourth sound track composed of low-frequency electronic impulses, programmed to match the activity on the screen, the way a music score highlights conventional action. Extra speakers pour the vibrations into the audience, approximating actual ground tremors. According to Watson, the system has been refined to the point where, at will, it can effect specific parts of the human body.

On June 7, 1974, "Sensurround" got a ringing if nervous endorsement from a group of disaster specialists touring the United States under State Department sponsorship. Representing twenty-three countries, they attended a showing on the Universal lot of selected scenes from the film, accompanied by the low-frequency sound system. Several of the shaken officials later said they found the demonstration "genuinely frightening."

They ought to know.

Another key wizard on *Earthquake* was matte artist Al Whitlock, considered by many to be the best in Hollywood. Matte shots (in-camera) are a sophisticated, tricky method of combining real action with miniature sets within the same shot. A cutout plate is inserted in front of the camera lens. This keeps certain parts of the film from being exposed. Later, another scene is exposed into the previously masked area. A counter-matte, conforming precisely to the outline of the matte, prevents double exposure of the previously photographed scene.

Some of the picture's most striking shots were the result of the matte process. When the tall electric towers snap and fall across the dry bed of the Los Angeles river, endangering Denise's young son Corry, mattes were used. The towers were actually less than eight feet high. The Wilson Plaza collapse merged an uncannily realistic miniature office building with cars and people in the foreground. The long panoramic shots of the ruined city after the temblor combined genuine vistas with ingeniously inserted mattes, supplemented by animated fires and smoke.

Easily the most spectacular full-size set in the picture consisted of the top six floors of Stewart Graff's office building, partially wrecked during the quake. To accommodate the eighty-foot-high structure, a twenty-foot-deep pit had to be dug in the floor of Universal's Stage 12, which is itself the size of a football field. It was to be the scene of some of the trickiest stunt work John Daheim has ever handled.

"There's a part of the picture where about thirty-five scared people come running down the fire stairs," Daheim declared. "They're supposed to be about twenty floors up, don't know that the stairs have fractured, and just fall off into space. The ones up front can't stop in time and take headers.

"Man, that's a hard one to stage! Even knowing there are airbags forty or fifty feet below, your natural reaction is to flinch, hesitate. But these people had to go over without even slowing down. God knows how many times Mark shot the scene before it went right."

Robson insisted on extraordinary safety measures on the set, spent hours rehearsing difficult action sequences. Five days of planning and rigging preceded the scene where Charlton Heston, Ava Gardner, and hordes of extras are bombarded with rubble from a collapsing office building. More than fifty special-effects men waited on catwalks far above the actors and stunt people, each of whom had been given a specific chalk mark to hit at a certain time. When the performer for which each special-effects man was responsible reached his mark, falling objects were released.

"A thing like this gets treacherous," Robson said later. "Up until the time we're ready for a take, we're on safety. When we're ready to make it, we take them off safety and watch everything like hawks. You can get killed if you make a mistake. Every scene is scary. Just as in real earthquakes, it's the unexpected that can be dangerous. We're lucky to have had so few mishaps."

Several stunt people were injured during filming. For example, a girl almost drowned during the flooding of the storm drain. A man fractured his skull when a wall of water slammed him against a concrete abutment in the dam-bursting sequence. "I went with him to the hospital," John Daheim recalled. "All he kept saying was, 'Don't worry about it, Johnny. I'm just lucky it never happened before.' You get kind of philosophical in this business."

According to Daheim, several of the stars insisted on performing their own stunts. Ava Gardner—firmly abandoning the "stately and beautiful" approach—herself drops from a high steel ladder into the pounding waters of the flooded sewer, is swept away. (The sewer set was a 125-foot-long tunnel dug between two small lakes on the Universal backlot. One of the lakes was at a lower elevation than the other, permitting the water to rush through the tunnel by gravity flow at a rate of 360,000 gallons per minute, controlled by wires. A wire net at the lower end of the tunnel prevented actors and stunt people from being washed into the lake. Special-effects men with scuba gear were on hand to aid anyone who got into trouble.)

Genevieve Bujold also performed her own stunts in several scenes. "She looks thin and fragile," Daheim declared, "but she did some marvelous things. When the earthquake starts, she grabs a tree, and just above her a stilt house collapses. Part of the house and a man roll down the hill, just miss her. It was dangerous, all right." Another scene called for the young actress to climb a steep, broken footbridge that has collapsed into the Los Angeles river. When the shooting was over, the front of her body and both arms were black and blue.

Lorne Greene and Monica Lewis, playing his secretary, refused doubles in the scene where they are lowered from the fractured office-building stairway while strapped in a swivel chair. "It took Monica about three days to get up the nerve," Daheim said. "It was quite a drop. But, like Lorne, she realized it would look phony if we used stunt people."

Among the technical innovations in the film was the work of special-effects man Frank Brendel. "Mark was complaining about the way some of the debris—supposedly concrete columns and such—bounced when it hit the ground. I had to find a way to solve the problem without killing the actors. It was easy. The fake rubble was mostly styrofoam. So I put in steel reinforcements and filled the individual pieces with sand. It gave the junk weight without making it heavy enough to brain somebody."

Not all of the rubble was fake, however. There's no practical way to duplicate some objects, like steel signs and large fragments of cement. The jagged chunk of concrete that misses Heston and Ava Gardner by less than six feet—crushing a car—weighed almost seven tons. Styrofoam filled with sand won't buckle a car roof.

The last shot of the film was the breaking of the Hollywood reservoir dam—that is, an eighty-foot-long replica of it built on the back lot at a cost of $70,000. Cliff Stine, heading a thirty-three-man crew, admitted nervousness. "It was a one-take shot," he told me. "We had nine cameras on it but I was jumpy anyway. If we messed up, the dam would be wrecked—and only another seventy thousand could put it back together again.

"We had fifty-three thousand gallons of water ready to spill into the reservoir behind the dam, more than enough to burst it. So in goes the water, and the cameras start turning. And the dam won't bust. It was a nightmare. We just stood there helpless, afraid the thing would go right after the cameras ran out of film. And then it busted, barely in time. Everybody applauded."

Coincidentally, minor earthquakes rocked Los Angeles on both the first and final days of shooting. The epicenter of the February 11 tremor was only a few miles from the real Hollywood reservoir dam, where Robson and his crew were filming. The menace of the dam was based on an incident still fresh in the minds of most of the film makers—the near-collapse of the Van Norman reservoir dam during the 1971 Sylmar quake. For days, more than eighty thousand people living in the reservoir's flood path huddled in high-school gyms and other evacuation centers while frantic engineers pumped water out of the disintegrating facility.

"For an instant I imagined the whole thing happening again," a crew member remarked afterward. "It would have been a weird way to go—washed away in a real flood while getting ready to fake one! Sort of loosens your grip on reality."

Late in June, I was in Los Angeles on other business. Mark Robson called me at my hotel, asked if I wanted to see a rough cut of *Earthquake*. Naturally, I did. I canceled an appointment and drove to the studio.

Robson, Bernard Donnenfeld, and Dorothy Spencer were waiting for me in the projection room. Dorothy had worked all night to complete the first cut, looked tired but relieved.

The film wasn't quite complete. Missing were a few of the key matte shots, photographed but still in the laboratories, and the musical score by John Williams. However, three minutes into the picture, I realized that it was going to be everything Lang, Robson, and I had hoped for. Even the scenes preceding the big quake were charged with tension and energy. Just as important, the picture lacked the pomposity that, for my taste, hurts most epic-sized productions. The action was clean and uncluttered, the camera never holding on a subject interminably while the director and producer congratulate themselves on their nifty sets and special effects.

"What I wanted was immediacy," Robson said after the screening. "Dorothy and I kept away from those endless dissolves that are supposed to tell the audience the production is 'important.' I don't know why endless dissolves are supposed to make a picture more important, but that's how some people figure. If it didn't contain action—or a promise of action—we cut it to the bone. Well, what do you think? Was it worth all those rewrites?"

"Yes," I admitted.

We went out for drinks, and Robson talked about his grandchildren. Bernie Donnenfeld recalled a perfectly lousy car—I think it was a Studebaker—that his father had driven in the late thirties. "I froze in that car every winter," he said. "We just couldn't make the heater work. Remember how cold your legs used to get when a car heater didn't work right?" That set me off on the rotten weather—heavy rains—we had been having back East.

The picture was barely mentioned at all. *Earthquake,* at last, was really done.